A-LEVEL YEAR 2

STUDENT GUIDE

CW00848466

EDEXCEL

Geography

The water cycle and water insecurity

The carbon cycle and energy security

Superpowers

Cameron Dunn and Michael Witherick

HODDER
EDUCATION
AN HACHETTE UK COMPANY

Hodder Education, an Hachette UK company, Blenheim Court, George Street, Banbury, Oxfordshire OX16 5BH

Orders

Bookpoint Ltd, 130 Park Drive, Milton Park, Abingdon, Oxfordshire OX14 4SB

tel: 01235 827720

fax: 01235 400401

e-mail: education@bookpoint.co.uk

Lines are open 9.00 a.m.–5.00 p.m., Monday to Saturday, with a 24-hour message answering service. You can also order through the Hodder Education website: www.hoddereducation.co.uk

© Cameron Dunn and Michael Witherick 2017

ISBN 978-1-4718-6408-7

First printed 2017

Impression number 5 4 3 2 1

Year 2020 2019 2018 2017

Cover photo: Kevin Eaves/Fotolia

Typeset by Integra Software Services Pvt Ltd, Pondicherry, India

Printed in Slovenia

Hachette UK's policy is to use papers that are natural, renewable and recyclable products and made from wood grown in sustainable forests. The logging and manufacturing processes are expected to conform to the environmental regulations of the country of origin.

Contents

Content Guidance

Questions & Answers

■ Getting the most from this book

Exam-style questions

Commentary on the questions

Tips on what you need to do to gain full marks, indicated by the icon ⓔ.

Sample student answers

Practise the questions, then look at the student answers that follow.

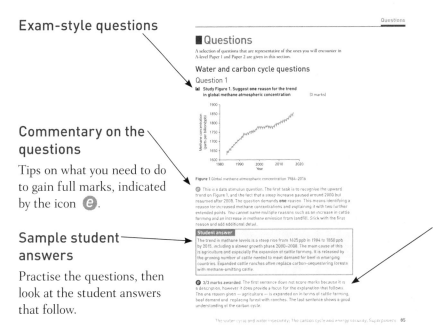

■ Questions

A selection of questions that are representative of the ones you will encounter in A-level Paper 1 and Paper 2 are given in this section.

Water and carbon cycle questions

Question 1

(a) Study Figure 1. Suggest **one** reason for the trend in global methane atmospheric concentration [3 marks]

Figure 1 Global methane atmospheric concentration 1984–2016

ⓔ This is a data stimulus question. The first task is to recognise the upward trend on Figure 1, and the fact that a steep increase paused around 2000 but resumed after 2008. The question demands **one** reason. This means identifying a reason for increased methane concentrations and explaining it with two further extended points. You cannot name multiple reasons such as an increase in cattle farming and an increase in methane emission from landfill. Stick with the first reason and add additional detail.

Student answer

The trend in methane levels is a steep rise from 1625 ppb in 1984 to 1850 ppb by 2015, including a slower growth phase 2000–2008. The main cause of this is agriculture and especially the expansion of cattle farming. It is released by the growing number of cattle needed to meet demand for beef in emerging countries. Expanded cattle ranches often replace carbon-sequestering forests with methane-emitting cattle.

ⓔ 3/3 marks awarded. The first sentence does not score marks because it is a description, however it does provide a focus for the explanation that follows. The one reason given — agriculture — is expanded on in terms of cattle farming, beef demand and replacing forest with ranches. The last sentence shows a good understanding of the carbon cycle.

The water cycle and water insecurity; The carbon cycle and energy security; Superpowers 85

Commentary on sample student answers

Read the comments (preceded by the icon ⓔ) showing how many marks each answer would be awarded in the exam and exactly where marks are gained or lost.

■ About this book

Much of the knowledge and understanding needed for A-level geography builds on what you have learned for GCSE geography, but with an added focus on key geographical concepts and depth of knowledge and understanding of content. This guide offers advice for the effective revision of **The water cycle and water insecurity**, **The carbon cycle and energy security** and **Superpowers**.

The water cycle and water insecurity, and The carbon cycle and energy security are tested in A-level Paper 1. The whole exam (including the other areas of study not covered here) lasts 2 hours and 15 minutes and makes up 30% of the A-level qualification. Superpowers is covered in Paper 2, which also lasts 2 hours and 15 minutes and makes up 30% of the A-level qualification. More information on the external exam papers is given in the Questions & Answers section at the back of this book.

To be successful in this unit you have to understand:
■ the key ideas of the content
■ the nature of the assessment material — by reviewing and practising sample structured questions
■ how to achieve a high level of performance within them

This guide has two sections:

Content Guidance — this summarises some of the key information that you need to know to be able to answer the examination questions with a high degree of accuracy and depth. In particular, the meaning of key terms is made clear and some attention is paid to providing details of case study material to help meet the spatial context requirement within the specification.

Questions & Answers — this includes some sample questions similar in style to those you might expect in the exam. There are some sample student responses to these questions as well as detailed analysis, which will give further guidance on what exam markers are looking for to award top marks.

The best way to use this book is to read through the relevant topic area first before practising the questions. Only refer to the answers and examiner comments after you have attempted the questions.

Content Guidance

This section outlines the following areas of the A-level geography specifications:

■ The water cycle and water insecurity
■ The carbon cycle and energy security
■ Superpowers

Read through the topic area before attempting a question from the Questions & Answers section.

■ The water cycle and water insecurity

Water is essential to life on Earth. It is important that we understand its global circulation and distribution, as well as the human demands on it. It is a scarce resource, and therefore its use needs to be carefully managed. Failure to do so promises water insecurity.

What are the processes operating within the hydrological cycle from global to local scale?

■ The global hydrological cycle is of immense importance to life on Earth.
■ The drainage basin is an open subsystem within the global hydrological cycle.
■ Water budgets and river systems are strongly influenced by the hydrological cycle.

The global hydrological cycle

A closed system

The global hydrological cycle is the circulation of water around the Earth. It is a closed system of linked processes so there are no external inputs or outputs. For this reason, the amount of global water is finite and constant. The only thing that does change is the state in which the water exists (liquid, vapour or ice). The proportions of global water held in each state vary over time with changes in climate.

The power that drives the global hydrological cycle comes from two sources:

1 solar energy: in the form of heat
2 gravitational energy: causes rivers to flow downhill and precipitation to fall to the ground

Stores and flows

Figure 1 shows how the global hydrological cycle works. It involves stores, flows and fluxes.

Knowledge check 1

Why is the global hydrological cycle a closed system?

Knowledge check 2

Name a climate change that would alter the proportion of water held in different states.

- Stores are 'reservoirs' where water is held. There are four main stores: (1) the oceans, (2) glaciers and ice sheets (cryosphere), (3) **surface runoff** and (4) the atmosphere. The oceans represent by far the largest store, followed by the cryosphere. Surface runoff consists of rivers and lakes, as well as **groundwater**. Of these freshwater stores, the cryosphere is the largest, accounting for 69% of all the global freshwater, followed by groundwater (30%). Less than 1% is stored in the biosphere (vegetation and soil moisture).
- Flows are the transfers of water from one store to another. There are four main flows: precipitation, evaporation, transpiration and vapour transport.
- Fluxes are the rates of flow between stores. The greatest fluxes occur over the oceans.

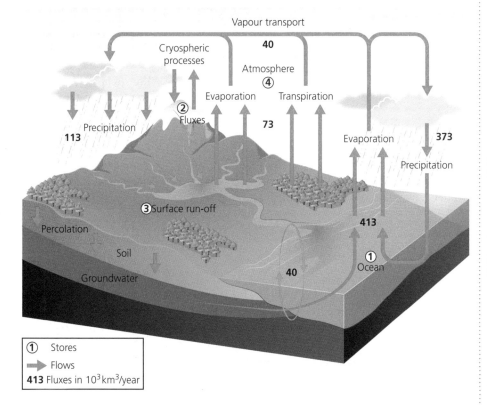

Figure 1 The global hydrological cycle

The global water budget

The global water budget takes into account all the water that is held in the stores and flows of the global hydrological cycle. The most significant feature of the budget is that only 2.5% of it is freshwater; the rest is in the oceans (Figure 2). Even more remarkable is the fact only 1% of all freshwater is 'easily accessible surface freshwater'. Nearly 70% is locked up in glaciers and ice sheets.

Although water is constantly circulating around the hydrological cycle, each store has a **residence time**. This is the average time a molecule of water will spend in one of the stores. Residence times vary from 10 days in the atmosphere to 3,600 years

Surface runoff, in this context, is an umbrella term for a number of land-based stores. These are rivers, lakes, groundwater and the moisture held in soils and vegetation.

Groundwater is the water contained within the soil and underlying rocks, and derived mainly from the percolation of rainwater and meltwater. It is a store, but water also moves through it, hence the term groundwater flow.

Exam tip

Sometimes flows are also referred to as transfers.

Exam tip

Be sure that you know the differences between the four flows: precipitation, evaporation, transpiration and vapour transport. You should already have come across them in your GCSE course.

Exam tip

It may be useful to be able to draw a quick, simple sketch of the hydrological cycle, showing its four stores and four flows.

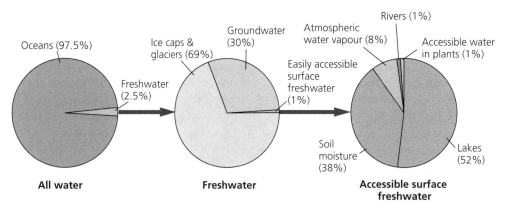

Figure 2 The availability of the world's water

in the oceans and 15,000 years in an ice cap. It is claimed that two water stores, **fossil water** and the **cryosphere** are non-renewable. The latter is to be questioned because, come another glacial period, more water will once again become locked in glaciers and ice sheets.

From a human viewpoint, the most critical feature of the global water budget is that accessible surface freshwater is a mere 1% of all the world's freshwater (Figure 2). This is the major source of water for human use. The smallness of this figure emphasises the important point that this water is not the abundant resource so many think it is. Indeed, as pointed out above, it is a scarce resource needing careful management.

The drainage basin

An open system

The **drainage basin** is a subsystem within the global hydrological cycle. It is an open system with external inputs and outputs. Since those inputs vary over time, so does the amount of water in the drainage basin (Figure 3). Drainage basins vary in size from that of a small local stream up to a huge river such as the Amazon. The drainage basins of tributary streams and small rivers nestle within the drainage basins of larger rivers.

Inputs

The main input is precipitation, which can vary in a number of different ways. All these characteristics can have a significant impact on the drainage cycle.

- **Form:** rain, snow or hail. Clearly, with snow, entry of water into the drainage system will be delayed.
- **Amount:** this will affect the amount of water in the drainage basin and fluxes within it.
- **Intensity:** the greater the intensity, the greater the likelihood of flooding.
- **Seasonality:** this is likely to result in the drainage basin system operating at different flow levels at different times of the year.
- **Distribution:** this is significant in very large basins, such as the Nile and the Ganges, where tributaries start in different climate zones.

Knowledge check 3

What are the main stores of easily accessible surface freshwater?

Fossil water is ancient, deep groundwater from pluvial (wetter) periods in the geological past.

The **cryosphere** is made up of those areas of the world where water is frozen into snow or ice.

A **drainage basin** is an area of land drained by a river and its tributaries, sometimes referred to as a river catchment. The boundary of a drainage basin is defined by the watershed.

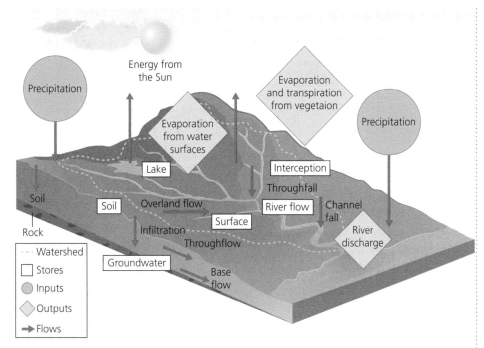

Figure 3 The drainage basin system

Exam tip

There are three types of precipitation (orographic, frontal and convectional). This distinction, made on the basis of causes is, however, less important than the five bulleted characteristics listed on the previous page.

Knowledge check 4

How does solar energy affect the drainage basin system?

Flows

There are at least seven flows that are important in transferring the precipitation that has fallen on the land into the drainage network (Figure 4).

1 **Interception:** the retention of water by plants and soils which is subsequently evaporated or absorbed by the vegetation.
2 **Infiltration:** the process by which water soaks into, or is absorbed by the soil.
3 **Percolation:** similar to infiltration, but a deeper transfer of water into permeable rocks.

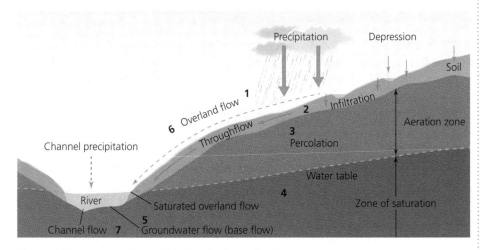

Figure 4 Flows operating within the drainage basin

Content Guidance

4 Throughflow: the lateral transfer of water downslope through the soil.

5 Groundwater flow: the very slow transfer of percolated water through pervious or porous rocks. Also known as **base flow**.

6 Surface runoff: the movement of water that is unconfined by a channel across the surface of the ground. Also known as **overland flow**.

7 River or **channel flow:** takes over as soon as the water enters a river or stream; the flow is confined within a channel.

Outputs

There are three main outputs of the drainage basin.

1 Evaporation: the process by which moisture is lost directly into the atmosphere from water surfaces, soil and rock.

2 Transpiration: the biological process by which water is lost from plants through minute pores and transferred to the atmosphere.

3 Discharge: (also known as **channel flow**) into another, larger drainage basin, a lake or the sea.

Impact of physical factors

Table 1 shows five significant physical factors. Climate mainly impacts on the inputs and outputs. The other four factors largely affect the relative importance of the different flows within the system. Of these flows perhaps the most important is surface runoff.

Table 1 Physical factors affecting drainage basin systems

Climate	Climate has a role in influencing the type and amount of precipitation overall and the amount of evaporation, i.e. the major inputs and outputs. Climate also has an impact on the vegetation type
Soils	Soils determine the amount of infiltration and throughflow and, indirectly, the type of vegetation
Geology	Geology can impact on subsurface processes such as percolation and groundwater flow (and, therefore, on aquifers). Indirectly, geology affects soil formation
Relief	Relief can impact on the amount of precipitation. Slopes can affect the amount of runoff
Vegetation	The presence or absence of vegetation has a major impact on the amount of interception, infiltration and occurrence of overland flow, as well as on transpiration rates

Impact of human factors

It is mainly human changes to (i) rivers and drainage and (ii) the character of the ground surface (its shape, texture and covering) that disrupt the drainage basin system, often by accelerating its processes (Table 2).

Table 2 Some impacts of human activities on drainage basin systems

River management	• Construction of storage reservoirs holds back river flows • Abstraction of water for domestic and industrial use reduces river flows • Abstraction of groundwater for irrigation lowers water tables
Deforestation	• Clearance of trees reduces evapotranspiration, but increases infiltration and surface runoff
Changing land use — agriculture	• Arable to pastoral: compaction of soil by livestock increases overland flow • Pastoral to arable: ploughing increases infiltration by loosening and aerating the soil
Changing land use — urbanisation (see more on p. 14)	• Urban surfaces (tarmac, tiles, concrete) speed surface runoff by reducing percolation and infiltration • Drains deliver rainfall more quickly to streams and rivers, increasing chances of flooding

Exam tip

It is important that you know these seven flows, their distinguishing features and their courses relative to the ground surface. Again, a simple sketch may serve as an aide memoire.

Knowledge check 5

What is the difference between throughflow and groundwater flow?

The components of the drainage basin system most affected by humans are:

- evaporation and **evapotranspiration**
- interception
- infiltration
- groundwater
- surface runoff

Amazonia

The Amazon basin contains the world's largest area of tropical rainforest. Deforestation here has disrupted the drainage basin cycle in a number of ways, including:

- a lowering of humidities
- less precipitation
- more surface runoff and infiltration
- more evaporation, less transpiration
- more soil erosion and silt being fed into the rivers

Water budgets and river systems

Water budgets

A water budget is the annual balance between precipitation, evapotranspiration and runoff. It is calculated from the formula:

$$P = E + R \pm S$$

where P is precipitation, E is evapotranspiration, R is runoff and S represents changes in storage over a period of time, usually one year.

The balance can be calculated at various scales, from global to local. Water budgets at a national or regional scale provide a useful indication of the amount of water that is available for human use (for agriculture, domestic consumption, etc.). At a local scale, water budgets can inform about **available soil water**. This is valuable to users, such as farmers, who can use it to identify when irrigation might be required, and how much.

Of course, as the caption for Figure 5 overleaf implies, soil water availability varies considerably from one climatic region to another.

River regimes

A **river regime** is the annual variation in the discharge or flow of a river at a particular point, and is usually measured in cumecs. The character of a river's regime is influenced by a number of variable factors (Figure 6):

- the size of the river and where discharge measurements are taken along its course
- the amount, seasonality and intensity of the precipitation
- the temperatures, with possible meltwater and high rates of evaporation in summer
- the geology and soils, particularly their permeability and porosity; groundwater noted in permeable rocks is gradually released into the river as **base flow**
- the type of vegetation cover: wetlands can hold water and release it slowly into the river
- human activities aimed at regulating a river's discharge

Evapotranspiration is the combined effect of evaporation and transpiration, such as occurs from most vegetated surfaces.

Knowledge check 6

What would be the effects of afforestation on drainage basin flows?

Available soil water is the amount of water that can be stored in the soil and is available for growing crops.

Content Guidance

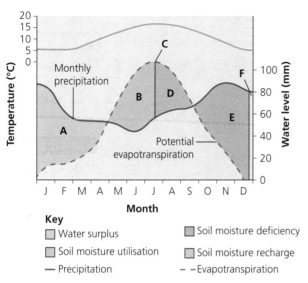

Knowledge check 7

How would the water budget graph for a location in the tropical rainforest differ from Figure 5?

Key
- Water surplus
- Soil moisture utilisation
- — Precipitation

- Soil moisture deficiency
- Soil moisture recharge
- – –Evapotranspiration

A Precipitation > potential evapotranspiration. Soil water store is full and there is soil moisture surplus for plant use. Runoff and groundwater recharge.

B Potential evapotranspiration > precipitation. Water store is being used up by plants or lost by evpaoration (soil moisture utilisation).

C Soil moisture store is now used up. Any precipitaion is likely to be absorbed by the soil rather than procedure runoff. River levels fall or rivers dry up completely.

D There is a deficiency of soil water as the store is used up and potential evapo-transpiration > precipitation. Plants must adapt to survive, crops must be irrigated.

E Precipitation > potential evapotranspiration. Soil water store starts to fill again (soil moisture recharge).

F Soil water store is full, field capacity has been reached. Additional rainfall will percolate down to the water table and groundwater stores will be recharged.

Figure 5 A water budget graph for a cool temperate location

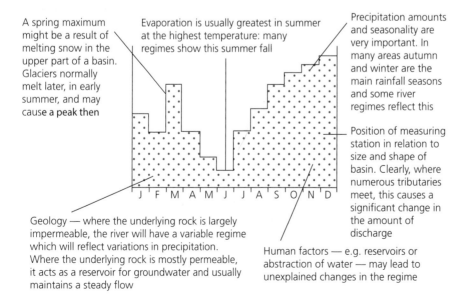

A spring maximum might be a result of melting snow in the upper part of a basin. Glaciers normally melt later, in early summer, and may cause a peak then

Evaporation is usually greatest in summer at the highest temperature: many regimes show this summer fall

Precipitation amounts and seasonality are very important. In many areas autumn and winter are the main rainfall seasons and some river regimes reflect this

Position of measuring station in relation to size and shape of basin. Clearly, where numerous tributaries meet, this causes a significant change in the amount of discharge

Geology — where the underlying rock is largely impermeable, the river will have a variable regime which will reflect variations in precipitation. Where the underlying rock is mostly permeable, it acts as a reservoir for groundwater and usually maintains a steady flow

Human factors — e.g. reservoirs or abstraction of water — may lead to unexplained changes in the regime

Figure 6 Factors affecting a river's regime

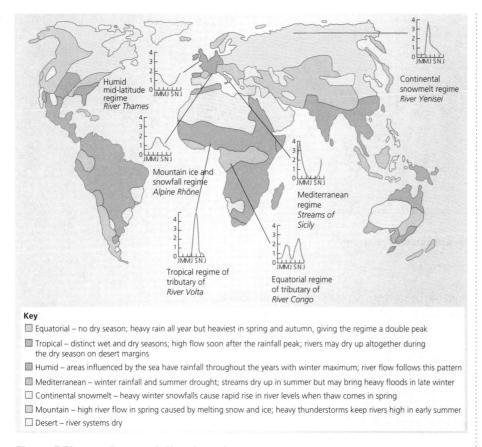

Key

☐ Equatorial – no dry season; heavy rain all year but heaviest in spring and autumn, giving the regime a double peak

☐ Tropical – distinct wet and dry seasons; high flow soon after the rainfall peak; rivers may dry up altogether during the dry season on desert margins

☐ Humid – areas influenced by the sea have rainfall throughout the years with winter maximum; river flow follows this pattern

☐ Mediterranean – winter rainfall and summer drought; streams dry up in summer but may bring heavy floods in late winter

☐ Continental snowmelt – heavy winter snowfalls cause rapid rise in river levels when thaw comes in spring

☐ Mountain – high river flow in spring caused by melting snow and ice; heavy thunderstorms keep rivers high in early summer

☐ Desert – river systems dry

Figure 7 River regimes and climatic regions

Figure 7 underlines the importance of climate in determining the basic character of river regimes.

Storm hydrographs

Whereas river regimes are usually graphed over the period of a year, storm hydrographs show discharge changes over a short period of time, often no more than a few days. The storm hydrograph plots two things: the occurrence of a short period of rain (maybe a heavy shower or storm) over a drainage basin and the subsequent discharge of the river.

Figure 8 shows the main features of a storm hydrograph:

- once the rainfall starts, the discharge begins to rise; this is known as the **rising limb**
- **peak discharge** is reached some time after the peak rainfall because the water takes time to move over and through the ground to each the river
- the time interval between peak rainfall and peak discharge is known as the **lag time**
- once the input of rainwater into the river starts to decrease, so does the discharge; this is shown by the **falling** or **recessional limb**
- eventually the river's discharge returns to its normal level or **base flow**

Knowledge check 8

Study Figure 7 and compare the river regimes of the River Yenisei and River Rhône. Suggest reasons for the differences.
....

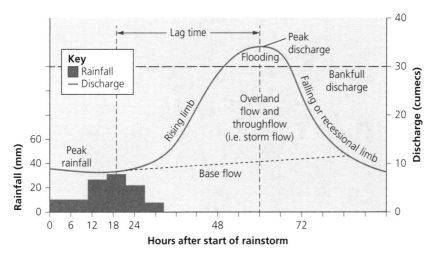

Figure 8 Features of a storm hydrograph

The shape of a storm hydrograph of the same river may vary from one rain event to the next. This variation is closely linked to the nature of the rainfall event. The shape of the hydrograph also varies from one river to another. This is the result of the particular physical characteristics of individual drainage basins (Table 3).

Some hydrographs have very steep limbs, especially rising limbs, a high peak discharge and a short time lag. These are often referred to as 'flashy' hydrographs. In contrast, there are some hydrographs with gently inclined limbs, a low peak discharge and a long lag time. These are often called 'delayed' or 'flat' hydrographs.

Urbanisation

When it comes to evaluating the factors affecting the character of storm hydrographs, particularly their 'flashiness', none is more important than urbanisation. Not least of its impacts is that it changes the basic character of the land surface. Its effects on hydrological processes include the following.

- Construction work leads to the removal of the vegetation cover. This exposes the soil and increases overland flow.
- Bare soil is eventually replaced by a covering of concrete and tarmac, both of which are impermeable and increase surface runoff.
- The high density of buildings means that rain falls on roofs and is then swiftly fed into drains by gutters and pipes.
- Drains and sewers reduce the distance and time rainwater travels before reaching a stream or river channel.
- Urban rivers are often channelised with embankments to guard against flooding. When floods occur, they can be more devastating.
- Bridges can restrain the discharge of floodwaters and act as local dams, thus prompting upstream floods.

In short, the overall impact of urbanisation is to increase the flood risk. The problem is made worse by the fact that so many towns and cities are located close to rivers. Historically, this was for reasons of water supply and sewage disposal. Often the historic nucleus was located at a point where a river could be easily crossed.

Exam tip

Draw a mind map of the ways in which urbanisation affects hydrological processes.

Knowledge check 9

Apart from a steady rainfall, what other factors contribute to a 'delayed' hydrograph?

Table 3 Interacting factors affecting the shapes of two different storm hydrographs

Factor	'Flashy' river	'Flat' river
Description of hydrograph	Short lag time, high peak, steep rising limb	Long lag time, low peak, gently sloping rising limb
Weather/climate	Intense storm that exceeds the infiltration capacity of the soil Rapid snowmelt as temperatures suddenly rise above zero Low evaporation rates due to low temperatures	Steady rainfall that is less than the infiltration capacity of the soil Slow snowmelt as temperatures gradually rise above zero High evaporation rates due to high temperatures
Rock type	Impermeable rocks, such as granite, which restrict percolation and encourage rapid surface runoff	Permeable rocks such as limestone, which allow percolation and so limit rapid surface runoff
Soils	Low infiltration rate, such as clay soils (0–4 mm/h)	High infiltration rate, such as sandy soils (3–12 mm/h)
Relief	High, steep slopes that promote surface runoff	Low, gentle slopes that allow infiltration and percolation
Basin size	Small basins tend to have more flashy hydrographs	Larger basins have more delayed hydrographs; it takes time for water to reach gauging stations
Shape	Circular basins have shorter lag times	Elongated basins tend to have delayed or attenuated hydrographs
Drainage density	High drainage density means more streams and rivers per unit area, so water will move quickly to the measuring point	Low drainage density means few streams and rivers per unit area, so water is more likely to enter the ground and move slowly through the basin
Vegetation	Bare/low density, deciduous in winter, means low levels of interception and more rapid movement through the system	Dense, deciduous in summer, means high levels of interception and a slower passage through the system; more water lost to evaporation from vegetation surfaces
Pre-existing (antecedent) conditions	Basin already wet from previous rain, water table high, soil saturated so low infiltration/percolation	Basin dry, low water table, unsaturated soils, so high infiltration/percolation
Human activity	Urbanisation producing impermeable concrete and tarmac surfaces Deforestation reduces interception Arable land, downslope ploughing	Low population density, few artificial impermeable surfaces Reforestation increases interception Pastoral, moorland and forested land

Synoptic themes

Planners have become important **players** in managing the impacts of urbanisation on the flood risk. This is because:

- many towns and cities are naturally prone to flooding because of their locations
- of the numbers of people who live in urban places and who therefore need protection
- of the huge amount of money invested in urban property

Flood risk management involves such actions as:

- strengthening the embankments of streams and rivers
- putting in place flood emergency procedures
- steering urban development away from high-risk areas such as floodplains

Exam tip

Draw a mind map of the factors affecting the shape of a storm hydrograph.

Knowledge check 10

Identify some other players involved in the issue of urban flooding.

What factors influence the hydrological system over short- and long-term timescales?

- Short-term deficits within the hydrological cycle (i.e. droughts) are the result of physical processes, but they can have significant impacts on people.
- Short-term surpluses within the hydrological cycle (i.e. floods) are the outcome of physical processes and can have significant impacts on people.
- In the longer term, climate change can have a significant impact on the hydrological cycle, both globally and locally.

Deficits within the hydrological system

Drought is defined in meteorological terms as a shortfall or deficiency of water over an extended period, usually at least a season. Meteorological drought is sometimes distinguished from hydrological drought. The latter is characterised by reduced stream flow, lowered groundwater levels and reduced water stores.

Drought can and does hit agricultural productivity particularly hard. This, in turn, can lead quickly to food shortages, famine and starvation.

While the causes of drought are basically physical, human activities can readily exacerbate the impacts of drought.

The physical causes of drought

The physical causes of drought are only partially understood. They lie somewhere in the complex interactions between atmosphere, oceans, cryosphere, biosphere and the land which produce the climates of the globe. Droughts can range from short-term and localised precipitation deficits to longer-term trends that are part of climate change.

Research suggests that **sea surface temperature anomalies** are an important causal factor in short-term precipitation deficits.

El Niño–Southern Oscillation (ENSO)

Temperature anomalies provide the key to the El Niño–Southern Oscillation (ENSO) which, in turn, is thought to trigger the occurrence of droughts. Figure 9 shows normal conditions in the Pacific basin and then conditions during an El Niño event. When this happens, cool water normally found along the coast of Peru is replaced by warmer water.

At the same time, the area of warmer water further west, near Australia and Indonesia, is replaced by cooler water. El Niño events usually occur every three to seven years and usually last for 18 months. El Niño events seem to trigger very dry conditions throughout the world, usually in the second year. For example, the monsoon rains in India and SE Asia often fail.

La Niña episodes may, but not always, follow an El Niño event. They involve the build up of cooler-than-usual subsurface water in the tropical part of the Pacific. This situation can also lead to severe drought conditions, particularly on the western coast of South America.

Sea surface temperature anomalies relate to how much temperatures of the sea surface, recorded at a particular time, differ from the long-term average. Anomalies may be positive or negative. A positive anomaly occurs when the observed temperature is warmer than the average. A negative anomaly is when the observed temperature is cooler than the average.

Exam tip

In the exam, you will be expected to know the difference between El Niño and La Niña episodes and how each contributes to drought conditions. But do not worry about the detailed mechanics of either.

A normal year

Warm, moist air rises, cools and condenses, forming rain clouds

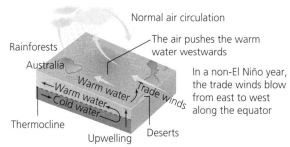

An El Niño year

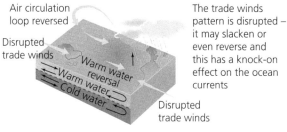

A La Niña year

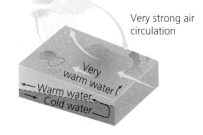

Figure 9 The workings of the ENSO

Human activity and the drought risk

Desertification in the Sahel

The point has already been made, but is worth repeating, that people are not the cause of drought as such, but their actions can make droughts worse and more severe. This is well illustrated by desertification in the Sahel region of Africa, stretching from Mauritania eastwards to Ethiopia (Figure 10).

The causes of desertification are essentially natural. They set in motion a downward spiral that runs roughly as follows:

- changing rainfall patterns with rainfall becoming less reliable, seasonally and annually (note the annual anomalies in Figure 10). The occasional drought year sometimes extends to several years
- the vegetation cover becomes stressed and begins to die, leaving bare soil
- the bare soil is eroded by wind and an occasional intense shower
- when rain does fall, it is often only for very short, intense periods. This makes it difficult for the remaining soil to capture and store it

Desertification is the process by which once-productive land gradually changes into a desert-like landscape. It usually takes place in semi-arid land on the edges of existing deserts. The process is not necessarily irreversible.

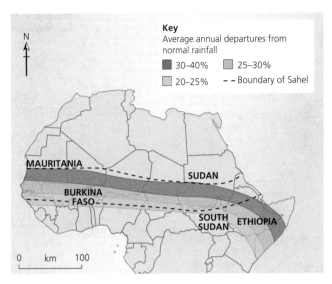

Figure 10 The Sahel region

Human factors do not cause drought but they act like a feedback loop. Humans enhance the impacts of droughts by the over-abstraction of surface water from rivers and ponds, and of groundwater from aquifers. Key human factors encouraging this are:

■ **population growth:** rapid population growth puts pressure on the land to grow more food. Migrants fleeing from one disaster area help to make another

■ **overgrazing:** too many goats, sheep and cattle destroy the vegetation cover

■ **overcultivation:** intense use of marginal land exhausts the soil and crops will not grow

■ **deforestation:** trees are cut down for fuel, fencing and housing. The roots no longer bind the soil and erosion ensues

In the case of the Sahel, the situation has been made worse by frequent civil wars. Crops, livestock and homes have been deliberately destroyed.

Drought in Australia

Drought is a recurrent annual feature in Australia, with up to 30% of the country affected by serious or severe rainfall deficiency. The link with El Niño events is well established. What is more worrying, though, is that droughts are becoming more frequent and more severe. To date, the worst event by far has been the 'Big Dry' of 2006. This was assessed as a 1-in-1,000-year event and is thought to have been associated with a longer-term climate change. But the important point here is that, unlike the Sahel, Australia has not followed the same downward spiral of desertification. A careful management of scarce water resources, and sorting out the competing demands of irrigation and urban dwellers, has stopped this happening. Other actions include the large-scale recycling of grey water, constructing desalinisation plants and devising new water conservation strategies.

The ecological impacts of drought

The concept of ecological resilience is crucial here. This is the capacity of an ecosystem to withstand and recover from a natural event or some form of human disturbance. Here the focus is on the impact of droughts on the resilience of two ecosystems — wetlands and forests.

Wetlands

Wetlands currently cover about 10% of the Earth's land surface and until 50 years ago they were considered as wastelands, only good for draining and infilling to provide building land. However, it is now understood that wetlands perform a number of important functions: from acting as temporary water stores to the recharging of aquifers, from giant filters trapping pollutants to providing nurseries for fish and feeding areas for migrating birds.

Drought can have a major impact on wetlands. With less precipitation there will be less interception (as vegetation becomes stressed), as well as less infiltration and percolation. Water tables will fall. Evaporation will also increase. This, together with the decrease in transpiration, will reduce the valuable functions performed by wetlands.

While droughts pose a threat to wetlands, the major challenge to their survival still remains artificial drainage.

Forests

Forests have significant impacts on the hydrological cycle. They are responsible for much interception which, in turn, means reduced infiltration and overland flow. Forests, of course, are characterised by high levels of transpiration.

Like wetlands, drought threatens forests, but it is people and deforestation that most threaten their survival. In the coniferous forests, drought is not only causing direct physiological damage but is also increasing the susceptibility of pines and firs to fungal diseases. Tree mortality is on the increase. The same applies to the tropical rainforest, except that the increased mortality attributed to drought appears to be having a greater impact on large trees. Here there is the added concern of what this increased tree mortality will eventually do to this incredibly important global carbon store (see p. 52).

As ecosystems play such a vital role within the hydrological cycle, it is important to ensure that their ecological resilience is not overstretched by either the destructive activities of people or natural events such as droughts and floods.

Surpluses within the hydrological cycle

The physical causes of flooding

Surpluses within the hydrological cycle more often than not mean flooding. The meteorological causes of flooding are:

- intense storms which lead to **flash flooding**, as in semi-arid areas but more commonly in mountainous areas
- prolonged, heavy rain, such as during the Asian monsoon and with the passage of deep depressions across the UK
- rapid snowmelt during a particularly warm spring, as on the plains of Siberia

Bangladesh is a particularly flood-prone country mainly because it is a land of floodplains and deltas built up by mighty rivers such as the Ganges, Padma and Meghna (Figure 11). These rivers are swollen twice a year by meltwater from the

Exam tip

Wetlands are a prime example of an undervalued ecosystem. You should understand the reasons why.

Flash flooding is distinguished by its exceptionally short lag-time — often minutes or hours.

Himalayas and by the summer monsoon. Hilly tracts between the rivers and behind Chittagong are often victims of flash floods.

Knowledge check 13

Suggest reasons why flash floods often occur in mountainous areas.

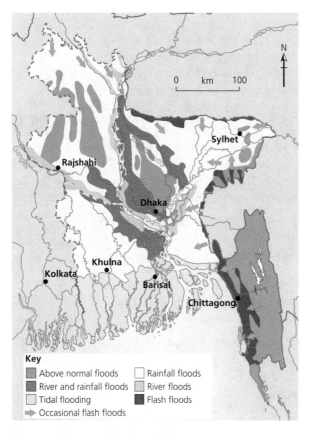

Figure 11 Types of flooding in Bangladesh

Figure 11 reveals yet another type of flooding — tidal flooding — often resulting from **storm surges** or when high river flows meet particularly high spring tides in estuaries. The likelihood of flooding is also increased by other physical circumstances:

- in low-lying areas with impervious surfaces, as in towns and cities
- where the ground surface is underlain by impermeable rocks
- when ice dams suddenly melt and the waters in glacial lakes are released
- where volcanic activity generates meltwater beneath ice sheets that is suddenly released (jokulhlaups)
- where earthquakes cause the failure of dams or landslides that block rivers

A **storm surge** is caused by very low air pressure which raises the height of the high-tide sea. Strong onshore winds then drive the 'raised' sea towards the coast, often breaching coastal defences and flooding large areas.

Human activity and the flood risk

A combination of economic and population growth during the twentieth century has caused many floodplains to be built upon and many natural landscapes to be modified for agricultural, industrial and urban purposes. The impacts of human activities on the hydrological cycle were examined on p. 10. These same activities, all related to changing land use within river catchments, frequently increase the flood risk (Figure 12), none more so than urbanisation (see p. 14).

Knowledge check 14

How else do plate tectonics contribute to flooding?

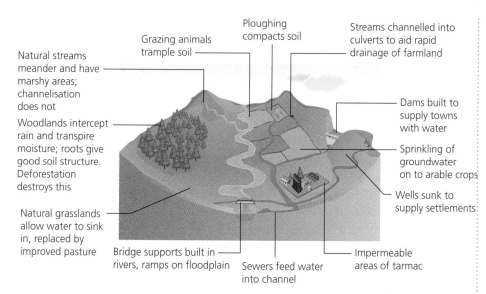

Figure 12 Human activities increasing the risk of flooding

One human activity not explicitly shown on Figure 12 passes under the umbrella title of river mismanagement. For example:

- **channelisation:** an effective way of improving river discharge and reducing the flood risk. The trouble is that it simply displaces that risk downstream. Some other location may well be overwhelmed by the increased discharge
- **dams:** block the flow of sediment down a river so the reservoir gradually fills up with silt; downstream there is increased river bed erosion
- **river embankments:** designed to protect from floods of a given magnitude. They can fail when a flood exceeds their capacity. Inevitably, when this happens, the scale of the flooding is that much greater

These examples of hard-engineering intervention serve as reminders that soft-engineering methods of reducing the flood risk are preferable. These include making greater use of floodplains as nature intended, namely as temporary stores of flood water, and using them only for nature conservation and perhaps agriculture and recreation.

The impacts of flooding

Socioeconomic

The impacts of flooding are all too familiar. They include:

- death and injury
- spread of water-borne diseases
- trauma
- damage to property, particularly housing
- disruption of transport and communications
- interruption of water and energy supplies
- destruction of crops and loss of livestock
- disturbance of everyday life, including work

Knowledge check 15

What is the difference between hard- and soft-engineering approaches to flood control?

Exam tip

Have some key facts about a particular flood event ready. They will add conviction to your answers.

Environmental

The environmental impacts of flooding receive much less publicity. Perhaps it is because there are some positives, which include:

- recharged groundwater stores
- increased connectivity between aquatic habitats
- soil replenishment
- for many species, flood events trigger breeding, migration and dispersal

Most ecosystems have a degree of ecological resilience that can cope with the effects of moderate flooding. It is where the environment has been degraded by human activities that negative impacts are more evident. For example, the removal of soil and sediment by floodwaters can lead to the **eutrophication** of water bodies. That same floodwater can also leach pollutants into water courses with disastrous effects for wildlife, while diseases carried by floodwater can weaken or kill trees.

UK floods 2007, 2013 and 2016

The UK has experienced some severe floods in recent years, most notably in the summer of 2007 and the winter of 2015–2016 (Figure 13).

These unusually severe floods have had the same basic cause, namely prolonged heavy rainfall, but at different times of the year. During the 2016 floods, large areas of the UK received more than twice the average amount of rainfall for that time of the year. Carlisle and Cockermouth in Cumbria were among the worst-hit places and were the focus of media attention.

As is so often the case after flood events, there were recriminations about the apparent inadequacy of flood protection measures. The following were singled out for blame:

- budget cuts in the amount of money being spent on flood defences
- an EU Directive that puts environmental conservation ahead of the regular dredging of rivers
- poor land management, resulting in blocked ditches
- global warming

What tends to be forgotten in post-flood enquiries is that flood protection measures are designed to cope with flood events of a given magnitude. When an event of a very rare order of magnitude occurs, no amount of money or engineering is going to provide the hoped-for degree of protection.

Eutrophication is the process of nutrient enrichment that ultimately leads to the reduction of oxygen in rivers, lakes and ponds, and the consequent death of fish and other species.

Exam tip

It is important to remember that the impacts of flooding are not all negative.

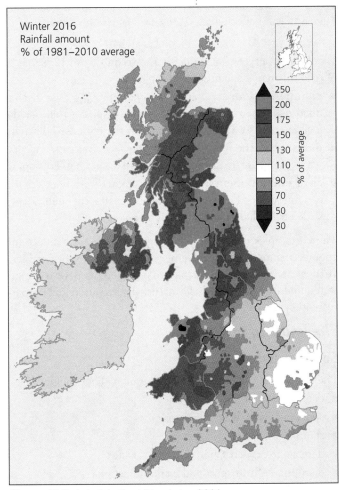

Figure 13 Rainfall in the UK, winter 2016

Source: contains public sector information licensed under the Open Government Licence v1.0

Climate change and the hydrological cycle

Impacts of climate change on inputs and outputs

Much research has yet to be done to establish beyond any doubt the impact of global warming and climate change on the hydrological cycle. Table 4 summarises the findings to date so far as the inputs and outputs are concerned.

Exam tip

Be cautious about the possible link between the increasing frequency of unusually severe floods in the UK and global warming.

Table 4 Summary of impacts of climate change on inputs and outputs

Precipitation	• A warmer atmosphere has a greater water-holding capacity • It is argued that the mode of precipitation may be more important than the amount in determining the impacts • Widespread increases in rainfall intensity are expected more than large increases in total amounts • Areas of precipitation increase include the tropics and high latitudes • Areas of precipitation decrease lie between 10° and 30° north and south of the Equator • The length and frequency of heatwaves is increasing in some locations and is resulting in the increased occurrence of drought • With climate warming, more precipitation in northern regions is falling as rain rather than snow
Evaporation and evapotranspiration	• Evaporation over large areas of Asia and North America appears to be increasing • Transpiration is linked to vegetation changes, which in turn are linked to changes in soil moisture and precipitation
Soil moisture	• Uncertain, as soil moisture depends on many factors, of which climate is only one • Where precipitation is increasing, it is likely that soil moisture will also increase

Impacts of climate change on stores and flows

Table 5 summarises some possible changes. There is less certainty here compared with Table 4.

Knowledge check 16

What is significant about soil moisture?

Table 5 Summary of impacts of climate change on flows and stores

Surface runoff and stream flow	• More low flows (droughts) and high flows (floods) • Increased runoff and reduced infiltration
Groundwater flow	• Uncertain, because of abstraction by humans
Reservoir, lake and wetland storage	• Changes in wetland storage cannot be conclusively linked to climate change • It appears that storage is decreasing as temperatures increase
Soil moisture	• Possibly little change, with higher precipitation and evaporation cancelling each other out
Permafrost	• Deepening of the active layer is releasing more groundwater • Methane released from thawed lakes may be accelerating change
Snow	• Decreasing length of snow-cover season • Spring melt starting earlier • A decreasing temporary store
Glacier ice	• Strong evidence of glacier retreat and ice sheet thinning since the 1970s • Less accumulation because more precipitation falling as rain • A decreasing store
Oceans	• More data on surface temperatures needed • Where there is ocean warming, there will be more evaporation • Possibly ocean warming leads to the generation of more cyclones • Storage capacity being increased by meltwater • Rising sea level

Concerns about short-term oscillations (ENSO cycles)

One of the problems with this forecasting of possible changes to the hydrological cycle is distinguishing between the impacts of long-term climate change and those of the short-term oscillations associated with El Niño events. A further complication results from the fact that ENSO cycles are associated with both extreme flooding in some parts of the world and extreme drought in others.

What is perhaps of more concern is the potential impact of short-term climate change (regardless of whether or not it is related to ENSO cycles) on global water supplies. Figure 14 suggests a scenario of increased uncertainty about the security of water supplies (for more, see the next section).

Knowledge check 17

Which stores are expected to increase?

Exam tip

Remember that some of the impacts in Tables 4 and 5 are possible rather than probable.

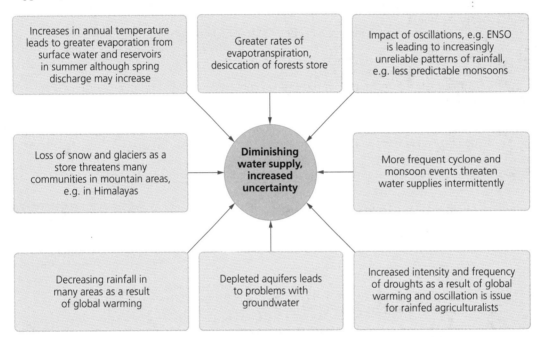

Figure 14 The impacts of short-term climate change on water supply

Synoptic themes

Figure 14 reminds us that we live in an uncertain world. Here the **uncertainty** arises simply because even modern scientific research is unable to make confident **forecasts** about the future availability of water. But even if scientists were able to do this, there are other important unknowns to be taken into account, such as possible advances in water technology and factors related to the demand side, such as population growth and the rising tide of global development.

Exam tip

Be sure you understand, say, three or four of the factors contributing to the uncertainty about future water supply in Figure 14.

How does water insecurity occur and why is it becoming such a global issue for the twenty-first century?

■ Water insecurity is a major concern for many countries and is the outcome of both physical and human factors.

- Water insecurity brings with it both serious consequences and considerable risks.
- There is a growing need for a more sustainable management of water supplies. This can be achieved by a number of different approaches.

The causes of water insecurity

The growing mismatch between water supply and demand

It is important to start by recalling the vital message conveyed by Figure 2 (p. 8), namely that accessible surface freshwater is a scarce resource. There is increasing pressure on that resource largely as a result of population growth and economic development. The situation is that many countries are experiencing water insecurity.

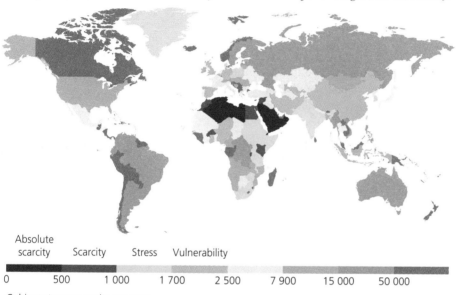

Absolute
scarcity   Scarcity   Stress   Vulnerability

| 0 | 500 | 1 000 | 1 700 | 2 500 | 7 900 | 15 000 | 50 000 |

Cubic metres per capita per year

Figure 15 The global distribution of renewable water resources

Water insecurity begins to exist when available water is less than $1,700\,m^3$ per person per day. This marks the start of what is known as **water stress**. Below $1,000\,m^3$ per person per day, water stress gives way to **water scarcity** (Figure 15).

The growing mismatch relates to the distribution of freshwater resources (water availability) and the distribution of the demand for water. Unfortunately, they do not coincide; far from it. This is where water insecurity begins. So let us focus first on these contributory factors: water availability on the one hand and the rising demand for water on the other.

Water availability

Water availability is conditioned initially by climate, i.e. by annual precipitation. That water is then moved and distributed by the drainage network. But there are a number of factors that reduce the amount of water that is eventually available for human use. These include both human and physical factors:

- evaporation and evapotranspiration
- discharge into the sea
- saltwater encroachment at the coast
- contamination of water by agricultural, industrial and domestic pollution
- over-abstraction from rivers, lakes and aquifers and the acute need to replenish these dwindling stores

Knowledge check 18

Study Figure 15 and identify five countries suffering from water stress.

Knowledge check 19

Suggest a definition for the term 'water availability'.

Because of these human factors, it is appropriate to talk of a diminishing water supply. The situation is also being exacerbated by global warming and climate change (see Figure 14 on p. 24).

Rising water demand

The rising demand for water is driven by three main factors:

- **population growth:** more people, more thirsts to quench
- **economic development:** increases the demand for water in almost all economic activities — agriculture, industry, energy and services. One of the biggest and fastest-growing consumers is irrigation (see more on p. 28)
- **rising living standards:** increase in the per capita consumption of water for drinking, cooking, bathing and cleaning. Added to this domestic consumption are water-extravagant things such as swimming pools, washing machines and dishwashers.

An important point here is that within the rising demand for water, there is increasing competition between water users for this dwindling resource. It is becoming increasingly serious in some locations. Figure 16 shows the three main pressures that are increasing the risk of water insecurity.

Exam tip

Be sure you understand how these three drivers increase the demand for water.

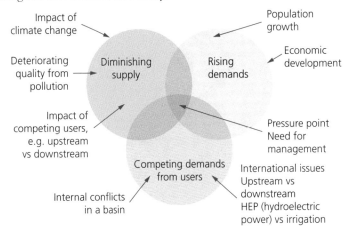

Knowledge check 20

Study Figure 16. What is meant by 'upstream vs downstream'?

Figure 16 Water insecurity in the making

Synoptic themes

It is important that every effort is made to identify those parts of the world which are in imminent danger of becoming victims of water scarcity. Who should do this? How confident can we be that the projections are accurate and reliable?

The consequences and risks of water insecurity

Water and economic scarcity

A distinction was made above between water stress and water scarcity. There is a further distinction to be made in water scarcity: that between physical scarcity and economic scarcity.

Physical scarcity occurs when more than 75% of a country's or region's **blue water** flows are being used. This currently applies to about 25% of the world's population.

Blue water is water stored in rivers, streams, lakes and groundwater in liquid form.

Qualifying countries are located in the Middle East and North Africa (Figure 17). Qualifying regions occur in north China, western USA and southeast Australia.

Economic scarcity occurs where the use of blue water sources is limited by lack of capital, technology and good governance. It is estimated that around 1 billion people are restricted from accessing blue water by high levels of poverty. Most of these people live in Africa (Figure 17).

In short, the causes of water scarcity are twofold:

1 a lack of precipitation, either annually or seasonally
2 a lack of the wherewithal needed to harness the amount of blue water in demand

Exam tip

The examiner may be impressed if you show that you know about these two types of water scarcity.

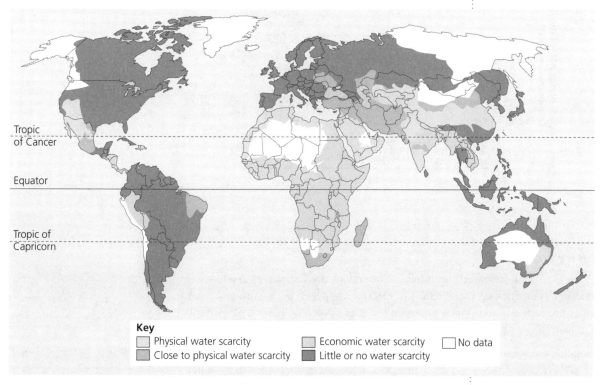

Key
- Physical water scarcity
- Close to physical water scarcity
- Economic water scarcity
- Little or no water scarcity
- No data

Figure 17 The global distribution of water scarcity

Access to **safe water** is regarded by some as a human right. In the twenty-first century, however, it is increasingly seen as a commodity for which a realistic price should be paid. This might be all well and good in the developed world. Indeed, much of the water supply industry there is now in the hands of private companies. People expect to have to pay for their water. In the developing world, however, the situation is very different. Supplying safe water in areas of physical water scarcity can be difficult, costly and well beyond the means of very poor people. This is where charities such as WaterAid provide such invaluable help. Their programmes are helping to reduce the extent of economic water scarcity.

Safe water is water fit for human consumption.

Exam tip

The price of water varies from place to place depending on the availability of water and the level of demand. It is when demand exceeds supply that the price rises.

Water supply and economic development

The point has already been made that economic development is one of the main drivers of the increasing demand for water.

Agriculture

Figure 18 shows the extent to which agriculture dominates water use. This is not surprising when it is understood that around 20% of the world's land is under full irrigation. Around 30% of this irrigation comes from dams and their networks of irrigation canals. But the majority of irrigation water is pumped from aquifers and is leading to massive groundwater depletion, especially in China, India, Pakistan and the USA. Clearly, this water situation is unsustainable and hydrological cycles are being seriously disrupted.

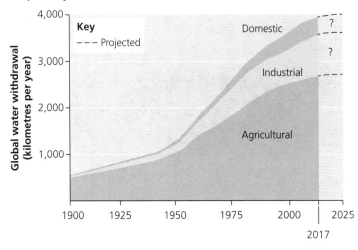

Figure 18 Trends in water use

Industry and energy

Just over 20% of all freshwater withdrawals worldwide are for industrial and energy production. Industries such as chemicals, electronics, paper, petroleum and steel are major consumers of water. Water pollution is a major problem associated with much of this industrial use of water.

Over half of the water used by energy production is either for generating **HEP** or as cooling water in thermal and nuclear power stations. So all this water is returned to its source virtually unchanged. However, there is mounting concern about the growth of biofuels for the production of bioethanol and biodiesel. Unfortunately these crops are very thirsty.

> **HEP** is the abbreviation for hydroelectric power.

Domestic use

With economic development comes rising standards of living and an increasing per capita consumption of water. Safe water is a fundamental human need. However, water does have its risks so far as human wellbeing is concerned. Water, particularly that polluted by a lack of sanitation, is an effective medium for the breeding and transmission of a range of lethal diseases, such as typhoid, cholera and dysentery. Water is also a productive breeding ground for some disease vectors, such as mosquitoes, snails and parasitic worms. Malaria, dengue fever and bilharzia are debilitating vector diseases. So safe water is vital to human health, particularly in the context of washing and food preparation.

From the above, it will be understood that an inadequate supply of water can easily impede any water-dependent aspects of economic development. Costs may well rise.

> **Knowledge check 21**
>
> Why do rising standards of living lead to an increase in per capita water consumption?

An inadequate water supply will also threaten human health. Environmentally, it will encourage people to over-exploit what water resources there are. This could easily prolong periods of drought and possibly be a first step on the downward path to desertification.

Potential water conflicts

When the demand for water overtakes the available supply and there are key stakeholders desperate for that water, there is potential for conflict, or what has been called 'water wars'. Within countries, conflicts can arise between the competing demands of irrigation, energy, industry, domestic use and recreation. But it is when countries 'share' the same river or drainage basin, as is the case with trans-boundary water sources, the 'normal' competition for water can be raised to a different level, namely one of international tensions and even open conflict.

Exam tip

Take care when using the world 'conflict'. In most instances, it means 'disagreement' rather than armed conflict. 'Tension' is a good alternative.

The Nile is a truly remarkable river. At 6,700 km, the Nile is the world's longest river. Even more remarkable is the fact that no less than 11 countries compete for its water. Currently 300 million people live within the Nile basin and such is the rate of population growth that total is set to double by 2030. All these people will need the waters of the Nile for domestic consumption and for growing crops. The Nile is also expected to generate HEP. Potential flash points have been the dams and barrages built in Sudan and Ethiopia that deprive downstream Egypt of its fair share of Nile water.

Other shared rivers that could become the battlefields of water wars are the Jordan and the Tigris-Euphrates in the Middle East, and the Indus and Ganges in the Indian subcontinent.

Knowledge check 22

Name the countries involved in each of these four shared rivers: Jordan; Tigris-Euphrates; Indus; Ganges.

Synoptic themes

Conflicts ranging from minor disputes to near wars can occur at any scale from local to international. At a local scale, key players are the water users (farmers, industrialists and households). Their views may well differ from those of planners, environmentalists and water providers. Internationally, the key players are those governments and users of trans-boundary water sources. In some case, it may be necessary to call in the mediating services of UN agencies.

Different approaches to managing water supply

Because of the wide range of players involved in the use of water resources, there are inevitable conflicting views as to what constitutes the best approach to the management of those resources. For example, economic players, such as businesses, typically opt for hard-engineering schemes, whilst environmental players, such as conservation organisations, favour a more sustainable approach.

Hard-engineering schemes

These require high levels of capital and technology. There are now up-and-running long-distance water transfer schemes; mega dams; and clusters of desalinisation plants.

Water transfers

Water transfer schemes involve the diversion of water from one drainage basin to another, either by diverting a river or constructing a large canal to carry water from one basin to another.

Perhaps the most publicised of these is China's South–North Transfer Project which is currently under construction. The idea of moving water from an area of surplus to one of deficit is a deceivingly simple one but, as Figure 19 shows, there are issues.

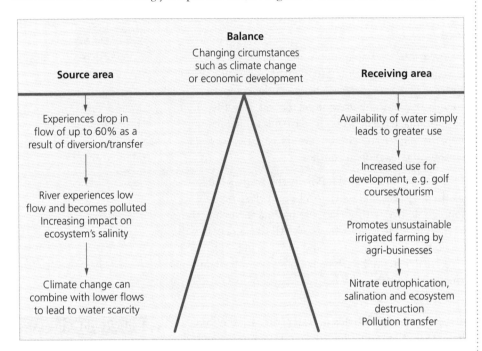

Figure 19 Water transfer issues

Mega dams

Nearly 60% of the world's major rivers are impeded by large dams, perhaps most notably the Colorado, Nile and Yangtze. While the capital costs of such dams are immense, this hard-engineering solution to water shortages has other drawbacks, such as the high evaporation losses from the water surface, the disruption of the downstream transport of silt and the displacement of people.

Desalinisation

Given the increasing pressure on freshwater resources and their shortage in the drier parts of the world, it is not surprising that some countries are looking to the oceans for water. Desalinisation has been undertaken on a small scale for centuries, but recently there have been technological advances in the process, most notably:

■ development of the process of reverse osmosis
■ pioneering work on carbon nanotube membranes

Desalinisation is an expensive process; it requires inputs of advanced technology and energy. However, as the price of freshwater rises, so some countries will look increasingly to the seas for their water supplies. Some Middle Eastern states, such as Saudi Arabia, Kuwait and UAE, have already done so.

Because of its inputs, desalinisation is classified as a hard-engineering solution. However, it is a sustainable process, although it does have an ecological impact on marine life.

Desalinisation is the process by which dissolved solids in sea water are partially or completely removed to make it suitable for human use.

Knowledge check 23

Why is desalinisation a limited option for increasing global water supplies?

Sustainable water management

The main aims of sustainable water managements are to:

- minimise wastage and pollution of water resources
- ensure that there is access to safe water for all people at an affordable price
- take into account the views of all water users
- guarantee an equitable distribution of water within and between countries

There is no silver bullet here. Rather, there is a diversity of actions being taken today as steps towards those four management aims. They include the following.

- **Smart irrigation:** a top priority given the huge amount of water used by irrigation. Traditional sprinkler and surface flow systems are being replaced by modern automated spray technology and advanced drip irrigation systems.
- **Hydroponics:** growing crops in greenhouses that are carbon dioxide and temperature controlled in shallow trays where they are drip-fed nutrients and water; there is no soil.
- Recycling of **grey water:** a low-cost option that produces water for agricultural use, but not human consumption.
- **Rainwater harvesting:** where people collect the rain falling on the roofs of dwellings and store it in butts for various domestic purposes, such as flushing toilets and watering the garden.
- **Filtration technology:** this is now so effective that there is little dirty water that cannot be physically purified and recycled.
- **Restoration:** of damaged rivers, lakes and wetlands so that they can play their full and proper part in the hydrological cycle.

These and other actions are clearly environmentally sustainable and can bring many socioeconomic benefits to local communities. The only question is: are they economically sustainable?

Singapore

Circumstances — few natural water resources, a thriving economy, a high standard of living and a high per capita consumption of water — have made water management a top priority in this tiny state with its nearly 6 million inhabitants. It has adopted a holistic approach to water management based on three key strategies:

1 collect every drop of water: the government has various ways of encouraging citizens to use water prudently. Since 2003, per capita domestic water consumption has fallen from 165 litres per day to 150 litres per day

2 re-use water endlessly: Singapore is at the cutting edge of new technologies to re-use grey water

3 desalinate more seawater: two desalinisation plants now meet 25% of the water demand

Despite these impressive actions, Singapore has to import water from neighbouring Malaysia.

Synoptic themes

Attitudes to water usage and supply vary. Some social players see the provision of safe water as a human right, whereas politicians see it as a human need which they have to supply. Businesses will secure their water needs almost regardless of the costs, whereas environmentalists insist that provision should be sustainable.

Integrated drainage basin management (IWRM)

IWRM (Integrated Water Resources Management) was first advocated in the late 1990s. It emphasises the river basin as a logical geographical unit for the management of water resources. It is based on achieving a close cooperation between basin users and players. The river basin is treated holistically in order to ensure three things:

- the environmental quality of the rivers and catchment
- that water is used with maximum efficiency
- an equitable distribution of water among users

Experience has shown that IWRM works well at a community level, but not so well in larger river basins, especially if an international boundary is involved, as is the case with the Colorado River and the Nile.

Water-sharing treaties and frameworks

In spite of the potential for conflicts over shared waters, particularly where there is 'greedy' upstream behaviour, international cooperation is the rule rather than the exception. Over the last 60 years, military conflict has occurred in only a handful of drainage basin disagreements. There has been a surprising amount of international cooperation, even between traditional enemies, as for example between India and Pakistan who share the Indus.

Important international agreements include:

- the Helsinki Rules with their 'equitable use' and 'equitable shares' concepts
- the United Nations Economic Commission for Europe (UNECE) Water Convention promotes the joint management and conservation of shared freshwater ecosystems
- the UN Water Courses Convention offers guidelines for the protection and use of transboundary rivers
- the EU Water Framework Directive (2000), committing all members to ensure the 'status' of their water bodies, including their marine waters up to one nautical mile from shore

In short, the potential for water wars is considerable and increasing with climate change. However, a commendable degree of international cooperation seems to be keeping the peace. But for how long?

Synoptic themes

Tensions and conflicts over water can occur at any scale from local to international. But the players involved can each play a part in reducing the conflict risk. At a global scale, the UN sets the rules which governments are required to observe. Non-governmental organisations (NGOs), such as the World Wide Fund for Nature (WWF), have a vital role to play in a 'neutral' monitoring of potential conflict situations. Transnational corporations (TNCs) have important responsibilities here. Locally, a range of players may be involved, from planners and environmentalists to water companies and water users. Each has a responsibility to minimise conflict and maximise cooperation.

Exam tip

As yet there are few well-publicised examples of IWRM. It is a neat idea, but …

Summary

- The global hydrological cycle is of enormous importance to all life on Earth. It is a closed system of stores and flows and is driven by solar energy and gravity. The global water budget determines the amount of water that is available for human use.
- The drainage basin is an open system within the global hydrological cycle. The system is often disrupted by human activities, such as deforestation, agriculture and urbanisation.
- Understanding water budgets, river regimes and storm hydrographs is important in the proper management of the land and water resources of drainage basins.
- Hydrological systems are constantly varying over a range of timescales. Recurrent droughts and floods are reminders of short-term variations or anomalies.
- In both instances, human activities have the potential to turn the deficits and surpluses of precipitation into hazards and sometimes disasters.
- The occurrence of droughts and floods is usually explained by scientists in terms of ENSO cycles. However, the increasing frequency and scale of these events is leading scientists to now look for explanations in much longer-term climate change.
- Climate change is undoubtedly already affecting the inputs and outputs of hydrological systems, as well as their stores and flows.
- Water insecurity arises out of a mismatch between the distributions of water supply and water demand. Its causal factors are both physical and human. An increasing demand for water is being driven by population growth, economic development and rising living standards. At the same time, the availability of water is being diminished by global warming and human abuse.
- Given that freshwater is a scarce but vital commodity, there is considerable potential for conflicts to occur between users within a country, and internationally over transboundary water sources.
- A proper management of water supply is crucial. It can be undertaken in a number of different ways. Some, such as hard-engineering schemes, are much less sustainable than water recycling or integrated drainage basin management schemes.
- Given that there are many 'shared' rivers, it is important that there are in place binding international agreements.

The carbon cycle and energy security

How does the carbon cycle operate to maintain planetary health?

- Most of the world's carbon is locked away in terrestrial stores as part of a long-term geological cycle.
- On shorter timescales, biological processes sequester carbon both on land and in the oceans.
- A balanced carbon cycle is important in sustaining other Earth systems, but the balance is being increasingly upset by human activities.

Terrestrial carbon stores

Carbon is everywhere: in the oceans, in rocks and soils, in all forms of life and in the atmosphere. Without carbon, life would not exist as we know it. The wellbeing and functioning of the Earth depends on carbon and how it cycles through the Earth's systems.

Stores and fluxes

Figure 20 shows the **carbon cycle** and its two main components: **stores** and **fluxes**.

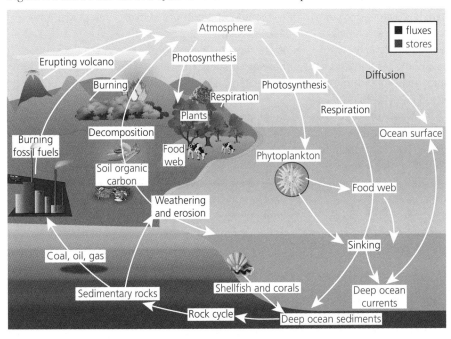

Figure 20 The carbon cycle

Carbon exists in different forms, depending on the store:

- atmosphere: as carbon dioxide (CO_2) and carbon compounds, such as methane (CH_2)
- hydrosphere: as dissolved CO_2
- lithosphere: as carbonates in limestone, chalk and fossil fuels, as pure carbon in graphite and diamonds
- biosphere: as carbon atoms in living and dead organisms

These stores vary in size and capacity, as well as in location. The important distinction in the biosphere is between terrestrial and oceanic locations.

Carbon fluxes, or flows, between the carbon stores of the carbon cycle are measured in either pentagrams or gigatonnes of carbon per year. The major fluxes are between the oceans and the atmosphere, and between the land and the atmosphere via the biological processes of photosynthesis and respiration. These fluxes vary not only in terms of their rates of flow but also on different timescales.

Geological origins

Most of the Earth's carbon is geological and results from:

- the formation of sedimentary carbonate rocks (limestone) in the oceans. The Himalayas form one of the Earth's largest carbon stores. This is because the mountains started life as ocean sediments rich in calcium carbonate derived from crustaceans, corals and plankton. Since these sediments have been upfolded, the carbon they contained has been weathered, eroded and transported back to the oceans

The **carbon cycle** is the cycle by which carbon moves from one Earth sphere (atmosphere, hydrosphere, lithosphere and biosphere) to another. It is a closed system but is made up of interlinked subsystems which are open and have inputs and outputs.

Carbon stores function as sources (adding carbon to the atmosphere) and sinks (removing carbon from the atmosphere).

Carbon fluxes (also known as flows or processes) are movements of carbon from one store to another; they provide the motion in the carbon cycle.

Exam tip

Be sure you know where carbon is stored and in what form.

- carbon derived from plants and animals in shale, coal and other rocks. These rocks were made up to 300 million years ago from the remains of organisms. These remains sank to the bottom of rivers, lakes and seas and were subsequently covered by silt and mud. As a consequence, the remains continued to decay anaerobically and were compressed by further accumulations of dead organisms and sediment. The subsequent burning of these fossil fuels has, of course, released the large amounts of carbon they contained back to the atmosphere

Geological processes releasing carbon

The release of geological carbon into the atmosphere results not just from people burning fossil fuels, but also through two natural processes:

1 carbon dioxide in the atmosphere reacts with moisture to form weak carbonic acid. When this falls as rain, it reacts with some of the surface minerals and slowly dissolves them, i.e. there is **chemical weathering**

2 pockets of carbon dioxide exist in the Earth's crust. Volcanic eruptions and earthquakes can release these gas pockets. This **outgassing** occurs mainly along mid-oceanic ridges, subduction zones and at magma hotspots

Biological processes sequestering carbon

Compared with its geological counterpart, biological **sequestering** operates on much shorter timescales — from hours to centuries.

Oceanic sequestering

The oceans are the Earth's largest carbon store. The oceanic store of carbon is 50 times greater than that of the atmosphere. Most of the oceanic carbon is stored in marine algae, plants and coral. The rest occurs in dissolved form.

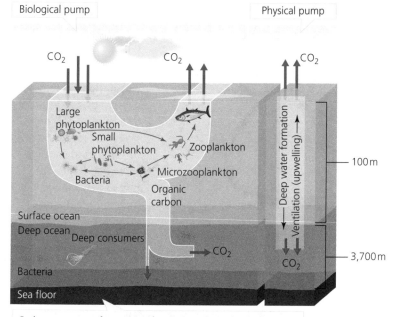

Carbonate pump: formation of sediments from dead organisms

Figure 21 Oceanic carbon pumps

Chemical weathering is the decomposition of rock minerals in their original position by agents such as water, oxygen, carbon dioxide and organic acids.

Outgassing is the release of gas previously dissolved, trapped, frozen or absorbed in some material (e.g. rock).

Carbon sequestration is the process by which carbon dioxide is removed from the atmosphere and held in solid or liquid form. It is the process that facilitates the capture and storage of carbon.

Carbon pumps are the processes operating in the oceans that circulate and store carbon.

There are three types of oceanic **carbon pump** (Figure 21).

1 Biological pumps move carbon dioxide from the ocean surface to marine plants (**phytoplankton**) by a process known as **photosynthesis**. This effectively converts carbon dioxide into food for zooplankton (microscopic animals) and their predators. Most of the carbon dioxide taken up by phytoplankton is recycled near the surface. About 30% sinks into deeper waters before being converted back into carbon dioxide by marine bacteria.

2 Physical pumps move carbon compounds to different parts of the ocean in downwelling and upwelling currents. Downwelling occurs in those parts of the oceans where cold, denser water sinks. These currents bring dissolved carbon dioxide down to the deep ocean. Once there, it moves in slow-moving deep ocean currents, staying there for hundreds of years. Eventually, these deep ocean currents, part of the **thermohaline circulation**, return to the surface by upwelling. The cold deep ocean water warms as it rises towards the ocean surface and some of the dissolved carbon dioxide is released back into the atmosphere.

3 Carbonate pumps form sediments from dead organisms that fall to the ocean floor. Particularly significant here are the hard outer shells and skeletons of crustaceans, fish and corals. All are rich in calcium carbonate.

Figure 22 shows the thermohaline circulation, a giant conveyor belt that moves water of varying temperatures and salinities through the oceans. As a consequence, it plays a vital part in the carbon cycle.

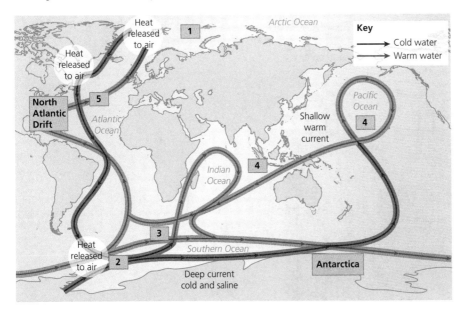

Figure 22 The thermohaline circulation

Terrestrial sequestering

Plants (i.e. primary producers in the ecosystem) sequester carbon out of the atmosphere during photosynthesis. In this way, carbon enters the food chains and

Exam tip

Use key words relating to the carbon cycle (such as store, flux, sink, pump, sequestration, etc.) in your answers.

Knowledge check 24

Name one carbon store and one carbon flux (or flow).

Phytoplankton consists of the microscopic plants and plant-like organisms drifting or floating in the sea (or freshwater) along with diatoms, protozoa and small crustaceans.

Photosynthesis is the process by which green plants and some other organisms use sunlight to synthesise (extract) nutrients from carbon dioxide and water.

The **thermohaline circulation** is the global system of surface and deep ocean currents driven by temperature (*thermo*) and salinity (*haline*) differences between different parts of the oceans (Figure 22).

Knowledge check 25

Name the three types of oceanic carbon pump.

nutrient cycles of terrestrial ecosystems (see Figure 20 on p. 34). When animals eat plants, carbon sequestered in the plant becomes part of their fat and protein. Respiration, particularly by animals, returns some of the carbon back to the atmosphere. Waste from animals is eaten by micro-organisms (bacteria and fungi) and detritus feeders (e.g. beetles). As a consequence, carbon becomes part of these creatures. When plants and animals die and their remains fall to the ground, carbon is released into the soil.

Carbon fluxes within ecosystems vary on two timescales:

1 diurnally: during the day, fluxes are positive — that is, from the atmosphere into the ecosystem; at night the reverse situation applies

2 seasonally: during winter, carbon dioxide concentrations increase because of the low levels of plant growth. However, as soon as spring arrives and all plants grow again, those concentrations begin to decrease until the onset of autumn

Biological carbon

All living organisms contain carbon; the human body is about 18% carbon by weight. In plants, carbon dioxide and water are combined to form simple sugars, i.e. carbohydrates. In animals, carbon is synthesised into complex compounds, such as fats, proteins and nucleic acids.

On land, soils are the biggest carbon stores. Here biological carbon is stored in the form of dead organic matter. This matter can be stored for decades or even centuries before being broken down by soil microbes (biological decomposition) and then either taken up by plants or released back into the atmosphere.

Soils store between 20% and 30% of global carbon. They sequester about twice the quantity of carbon as the atmosphere and three times that of terrestrial vegetation. The actual amount of carbon stored in a soil depends on:

- climate: this dictates the rates of plant growth and decomposition; both increase with temperature and rainfall
- vegetation cover: this affects the supply of dead organic matter, being heaviest in tropical rainforests and least in the tundra
- soil type: clay protects carbon from decomposition, so clay-rich soils have a higher carbon content
- land use: cultivation and other forms of soil disturbance increase the rate of carbon loss

Increasing human interference

A fully functioning and balanced carbon cycle is vital to the health of the Earth in sustaining its other systems. It plays a key role in regulating the Earth's temperature by controlling the amount of carbon dioxide in the atmosphere. This, in turn, affects the hydrological cycle. Ecosystems, terrestrial and oceanic, also depend on the carbon cycle. All this is a consequence of the fact that the carbon cycle provides the all-important link between the atmosphere, hydrosphere, lithosphere and biosphere. But the carbon balance is being increasingly altered by human actions and activities.

Exam tip

Make sure you know the differences between sequestering and photosynthesis.

Exam tip

Remember that soils both sequester and release carbon dioxide. The balance between the two fluxes varies with local conditions, such as climate, soil type, vegetation cover and land use.

Knowledge check 26

What factors affect the amount of carbon stored in the soil?

The greenhouse effect

It is the increasing concentration of carbon in the atmosphere that is causing great concern. Carbon dioxide and methane are perhaps the most important of all the greenhouse gases (GHGs). Their increasing presence in the atmosphere is upsetting the Earth's natural temperature-control system, resulting in the greenhouse effect (Figure 23).

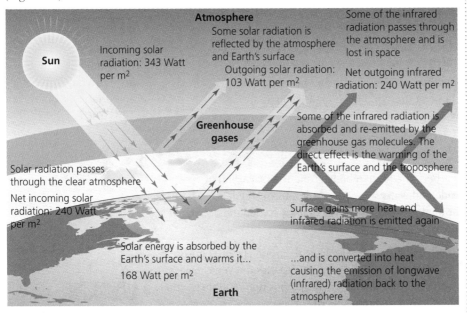

Figure 23 The greenhouse effect

The Earth's climate is driven by incoming short-wave solar radiation:

- 31% is reflected back into space by clouds, GHGs and by the land surface
- the remaining 69% is absorbed at the Earth's surface, especially by the oceans
- much of this radiation absorbed at the surface is re-radiated as long-wave radiation
- large amounts of this long-wave radiation are, however, prevented from returning into space by clouds and GHGs
- the trapped long-wave radiation is then re-radiated back to the Earth's surface

It is this trapped, re-radiated, long-wave energy that constitutes the natural greenhouse effect and controls the mean global temperature. It also determines the distributions of both heat and precipitation.

Maintaining a balanced carbon cycle

A balanced carbon cycle is the outcome of different components working in a sort of harmony with each other. Here we focus on just two of those components — photosynthesis and soil health.

Photosynthesis

Photosynthesis (see definition on p. 36) by terrestrial and oceanic organisms plays an essential role in keeping carbon dioxide levels relatively constant and thereby helping to regulate the Earth's mean temperature.

Greenhouse gases (GHGs) are primarily water vapour, carbon dioxide, methane, nitrous oxide and ozone. These gases both absorb and emit solar radiation and, in so doing, create the so-called **greenhouse effect** that determines global temperatures.

Knowledge check 27

What are the main GHGs?

Exam tip

Sometimes it can be quicker and easier to produce a simplified and annotated diagram of the greenhouse effect in the exam.

The amount of photosynthesis varies spatially, particularly with **net primary productivity (NPP)**. NPP is highest in the warm and wet parts of the world, particularly in the tropical rainforests and in shallow ocean waters. It is least in the tundra and boreal forests.

Soil health

Soil health is an important aspect of ecosystems and a key element in the normal functioning of the carbon cycle. Soil health depends on the amount of organic carbon stored in the soil. The storage amount is determined by the balance between the soil's inputs (plant and animal remains, nutrients) and its outputs (decomposition, erosion and uptake by plant and animal growth).

Carbon is the main component of soil organic matter and helps to give soil its moisture-retention capacity, its structure and its fertility. Organic carbon is concentrated in the surface layer of the soil. A healthy soil has a large surface reservoir of available nutrients which, in their turn, condition the productivity of ecosystems. All this explains why even a small amount of surface soil erosion can have such a devastating impact on soil health and fertility.

Fossil fuel combustion

Fossil fuels have been burnt to provide energy and power at increasing rates since the beginning of the Industrial Revolution in the mid-eighteenth century. Fossil fuel combustion is the number one threat to the global carbon cycle. It is changing the balance of both the carbon stores and the fluxes.

It is estimated that about half the extra emissions of carbon dioxide since 1750 have remained in the atmosphere. The rest has been fluxed from the atmosphere into the stores provided by the oceans, ecosystems and soils. The rate of carbon fluxing has speeded up. It is that additional carbon dioxide in the atmosphere and its impact on the greenhouse effect that is largely responsible for a number of climate changes:

- a rise in the mean global temperature
- more precipitation and evaporation
- sudden shifts in weather patterns
- more extreme weather events, such as floods, storm surges and droughts
- the nature of climate change is varying from region to region — some areas are becoming warmer and drier, others wetter

These changes in climate have serious knock-on effects on:

- sea level: this is rising because of melting ice sheets and glaciers; many major coastal cities around the world are under threat from flooding by the sea
- ecosystems: a decline in the goods and services they provide; a decline in biodiversity; changes in the distributions of species; marine organisms threatened by lower oxygen levels and ocean acidification; the bleaching of corals, etc.
- the hydrological cycle: increased temperatures and evaporation rates cause more moisture to circulate around the cycle

Net primary productivity (NPP) is the amount of organic matter that is available for humans and other animals to harvest or consume.

Knowledge check 28

What helps keep carbon dioxide levels in the atmosphere fairly constant?

Knowledge check 29

What are the fossil fuels?

Exam tip

Draw a simple annotated spider diagram summarising some of the impacts of climate change. Such a diagram could be useful in structuring and supporting an exam answer.

Knowledge check 30

Why is climate change causing the distributions of plant and animal species to change?

What are the consequences for people and the environment of our increasing demand for energy?

- In an energy-hungry modern world, achieving energy security is becoming a top priority for many countries.
- A combination of increasing population, economic development and rising living standards is creating a huge and almost insatiable demand for energy. That demand is being largely met by the burning of fossil fuels.
- There are alternative sources of energy but they all have their costs as well as benefits.

Energy security

Energy security is a something that all countries seek to achieve. The most secure energy situation is one where the national demand for energy can be completely satisfied from domestic sources. The more a country depends on imported energy, the more it is exposed to risks of an economic and geopolitical kind. Four key aspects of energy security are (Figure 24):

- availability
- accessibility
- affordability
- reliability

Energy security is achieved when there is an uninterrupted availability of energy at a national level and at an affordable price.

Knowledge check 31

What is meant by the 'accessibility of energy'?

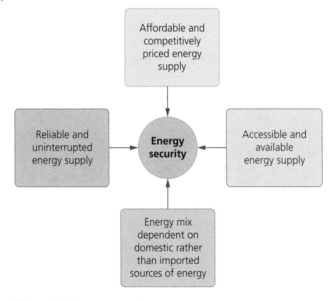

Figure 24 Energy security

The importance of energy security stems from the fact that energy is vital to the functioning of a country. For example, it:

- powers most forms of transport
- lights settlements
- is used by some types of commercial agriculture
- warms or cools homes and powers domestic appliances

Knowledge check 32

What types of commercial farming need a large input of energy?

- is vital to modern communications
- drives most forms of manufacturing

The energy mix

Figure 24 refers to energy mix. It is an important component of energy security. Clearly, the mix or proportions of different energy sources will vary from country to country. Some important distinctions can be made here, for example between:

- domestic and foreign (imported) sources
- primary and secondary energy sources

Most energy today is consumed in the form of electricity. The main primary energy sources used to generate electricity are:

- non-renewable fossil fuels, such as coal, oil and natural gas
- recyclable fuels, such as nuclear energy, general waste and biomass
- renewable energies, such as water, wind, solar, geothermal and tidal

Figure 25 shows how the global primary energy mix has changed since 1820 as energy consumption has risen.

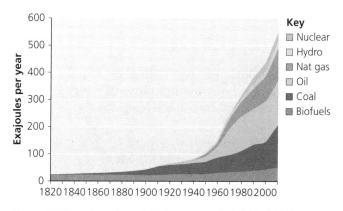

Figure 25 The changing global energy mix (1820–2010)

The consumption of energy

The consumption of energy is measured in two ways:

1 in per capita terms, i.e. as kilogrammes of oil equivalent or megawatt hours per person. In general, this measure rises with economic development

2 by a measure known as **energy intensity**, which is assessed by calculating the units of energy used per unit of GDP. The fewer the units of energy, the more efficiently a country is using its energy supply. In general, energy intensity values decrease with economic development

Figure 26 shows some of the factors affecting per capita energy consumption. The upper five factors in the diagram have already been touched on and need little further explanation, but the lower three perhaps do.

Energy mix is the combination of different energy sources available to meet a country's total energy demand.

Primary energy is any form of energy found in nature that has not been subject to any conversion or transformation. Primary energy can be renewable (water and wind power) or non-renewable (coal, oil and gas).

Secondary energy refers to the more convenient forms of energy, such as electricity, which are derived from the transformation or conversion of primary energy sources.

Exam tip

There may be questions in the exam where you should show that you are aware of this distinction between primary and secondary energy.

Knowledge check 33

Define the term 'recyclable energy'.

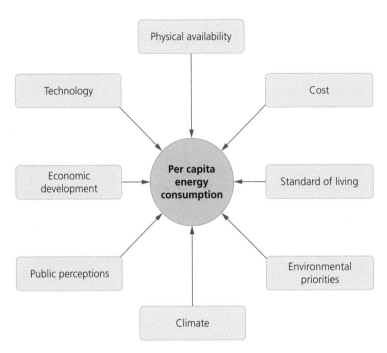

Figure 26 Some factors affecting per capita energy consumption

Knowledge check 34

What are the advantages of converting primary energy sources into electricity?

- **Public perceptions** of, or attitudes towards, energy differ. For some consumers, energy is perceived almost as a human right and there to be used with little or no regard for the environmental consequences. Others give priority to minimising the wastage of energy and maximising sustainability.
- **Climate** is a very significant factor. Very high levels of consumption in North America, the Middle East and Australia reflect the extra energy needed to make the extremes of heat and cold more comfortable — in the home, at work and in public places.
- **Environmental priorities** of governments. For some, the energy policy will be one of taking the cheapest route to meeting the nation's energy needs, regardless of the environmental costs. Others will seek to increase their reliance on renewable sources of energy; while still others will have in place policies that raise energy efficiency and energy saving.

Energy portraits of France versus USA

The USA and France rank second and tenth in the league table of energy consumers respectively, but total energy consumption in France is only one-tenth that of the USA. The difference is largely explained by differences in population — 318.9 million in the USA compared with 64.6 million in France. In per capita terms, the USA tops the rankings while France is placed sixth.

Figure 27 compares France and the USA in terms of their sources of primary energy. In the USA, over three-quarters of the energy comes from fossil fuels. The French energy mix is very different, with half its energy coming from fossil fuels and around 40% coming from nuclear energy. In terms of energy security, France is much less well placed than the USA, if only because nearly half of its primary energy is imported. The USA is much more self-sufficient.

Knowledge check 35

How does technology affect per capita energy consumption?

Knowledge check 36

Why is the USA less dependent on nuclear energy than France?

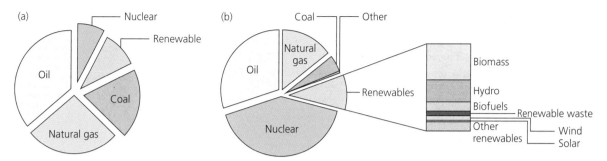

Figure 27 Energy consumption by primary source: (a) USA and (b) France

Energy players

Synoptic themes

Meeting the demand for energy involves **energy pathways** from producer to consumer. At both ends of such pathways, there are influential players (organisations, groups or individuals) with a particular involvement in the energy business. At the supply end, there are energy companies and the governments of energy-producing countries. There are governments at the demand end also, as well as a range of consumers from industrial to domestic. Along the pathways, there are companies responsible for the movement and processing of energy. For more on energy pathways see p. 44.

Table 6 sets out the major players in the world of energy. Of particular importance here is OPEC.

> An **energy pathway** is the route taken by any form of energy from its source to its point of consumption. The routes involve different forms of transport, such as tanker ships, pipelines and electricity transmission grids.

Table 6 Major players in the world of energy

Player	Role
Transnational corporations (TNCs)	The big names in the oil and gas business include Gazprom, ExxonMobil, PetroChina and Royal Dutch Shell. Nearly half of the top 20 companies are state-owned (all or in part) and, therefore, very much under government control. Because of this, strictly speaking they are not TNCs. Most are involved in a range of operations: exploring, extracting, transporting, refining and producing petrochemicals
Organisation of the Petroleum Exporting Countries (OPEC)	OPEC has twelve member countries which between them own around two-thirds of the world's oil reserves. Because of this, it is in a position to control the amount of oil and gas entering the global market, as well as the prices of both commodities. OPEC has been accused of holding back production in order to drive up oil and gas prices
Energy companies	Important here are the companies that convert primary energy (oil, gas, water and nuclear) into electricity and then distribute it. Most companies are involved in the distribution of both gas and electricity. They have considerable influence when it comes to setting consumer prices and tariffs
Consumers	An all-embracing term, but probably the most influential consumers are transport, industry and domestic users. Consumers are largely passive players when it comes to fixing energy prices
Governments	They can play a number of different roles; they are the guardians of national energy security and can influence the sourcing of energy for geopolitical reasons

Reliance on fossil fuels

Despite mounting global concern about increasing carbon emissions and their contribution to climate change, the world continues to rely on fossil fuels (coal, oil and gas) for the greater part of its energy needs.

> **Exam tip**
>
> Be sure you understand why OPEC is such a powerful player in the global energy business.

Mismatch between fossil fuel supply and demand

A fundamental feature of the world of energy is that the distributions of fossil fuel supply and demand do not coincide. This important point is confirmed by Tables 7, 8 and 9, which set out the top ten producers and consumers of each of the three main fossil fuels.

Table 7 The world's leading coal producers and consumers

Coal production		Coal consumption	
Country	Production (m tonnes)	Country	Consumption (m tonnes)
China	3,650.0	China	1,839.4
USA	922.1	USA	502.1
India	605.8	Japan	117.6
Australia	431.2	South Africa	93.1
Indonesia	386.0	Russia	91.0
Russia	354.8	South Korea	79.6
South Africa	260.0	Germany	77.6
Germany	192.3	Poland	59.8
Poland	144.1	Australia	49.6
Kazakhstan	116.4	Indonesia	43.7

Table 8 The world's leading crude oil producers and importers

Oil production		Oil imported	
Country	Production (m barrels per day)	Country	Imported (m barrels per day)
Russia	10.3	China	6.1
Saudi Arabia	10.1	USA	5.1
USA	8.7	Japan	4.2
Iraq	4.8	India	2.7
China	3.9	South Korea	2.3
Iran	3.9	Germany	2.2
Canada	3.9	France	1.6
UAE	3.2	Spain	1.2
Kuwait	3.0	Italy	1.1
Brazil	2.6	Netherlands	1.1

Energy pathways

It should now be clear from Tables 7, 8 and 9 that there are basic mismatches between the distributions of production and consumption of all three main fossil fuels. These mismatches are resolved by the creation of **energy pathways** (see p. 43) that allow transfers to take place between producers and consumers. The main fossil fuel pathways are:

- coal: from six main producers (Australia, Indonesia, Russia, South Africa, Colombia and USA) to four major markets (EU, India, China and Japan-Korea-Taiwan)

Table 9 The world's leading gas producers and importers

Gas production		Gas imported	
Country	(000 million m³)	Country	(000 million m³)
USA	4,359	Germany	100
Russia	670	Japan	98
Iran	163	Italy	70
Canada	143	UK	54
Qatar	133	South Korea	47
Norway	115	France	46
China	107	USA	45
Saudi Arabia	103	Russia	38
Algeria	83	Turkey	38
Netherlands	81	Spain	37

- oil: from producers in the Middle East to four major markets (EU, USA and E and SE Asia); lesser producers are Nigeria and Venezuela
- gas: from major producers in the Middle East and from Russia to markets in Europe; lesser producers are Indonesia, Nigeria and Trinidad

Russian gas to Europe

Energy pathways are a key aspect of energy security but can be prone to disruption, especially as conventional fossil fuels have to be moved over long distances from sources to markets. Table 9 shows that Russia is currently the second largest producer of gas. Most of its gas exports go to European countries (five are shown amongst the ten largest importers). Russian gas is delivered to Europe mainly through five pipelines.

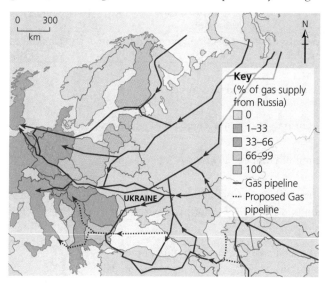

Figure 28 The delivery of Russian gas to the EU, 2012

Geopolitically significant is the fact that three of those pipelines cross Ukraine, a country from which Russia has recently annexed the Crimea (Figure 28). It also now occupies parts of eastern Ukraine. Clearly, Ukraine might be in a position of strength here. It

Russia has taken Crimea which was Ukraines

could increase its charges for allowing Russian gas to pass through it. It could even stop the gas flows altogether. This potential threat seems to leave Russia with two options:

1   reduce delivery of gas through these threatened pipelines and export more through two northern pipelines that run through Finland and Poland

2   annexe the whole of Ukraine

Given the history of strained political relations between Russia and Western Europe, it would appear strategically unwise for EU countries to become heavily reliant on Russian gas. Although the UK still obtains most of its gas from Qatar, it has recently substantially increased its imports of Russian gas in order to offset the declining output of gas from its North Sea gas fields.

Knowledge check 37

Why is the output from the UK's gas fields in the North Sea declining?

Unconventional fossil fuels

Despite the need to move the global energy budget towards renewable energy sources, much exploration work is still going on searching for new oil and gas fields. At the same time, attention is turning towards what are called 'unconventional fossil fuels'. There are four: tar sands, oil shale, shale gas and deepwater oil. Canada is leading the way with the first of these, the USA with the second and third, and Brazil with the last (Table 10).

Table 10 Unconventional sources of fossil fuel

Resource	Nature	Extraction
Tar sands	A mixture of clay, sand, water and bitumen (a heavy, viscous oil)	Tar sands have to be mined and then injected with steam to make the tar less viscous so that it can be pumped out
Oil shale	Oil-bearing rocks that are permeable enough to allow the oil to be pumped out directly	Either mined, or shale is ignited so that the light oil fractions can be pumped out
Shale gas	Natural gas that is trapped in fine-grained sedimentary rocks	Fracking: pumping in water and chemicals forces out the gas
Deepwater oil	Oil and gas that is found well offshore and at considerable oceanic depths	Drilling takes place from ocean rigs; already underway in the Gulf of Mexico and off Brazil

It is important to note that exploitation of these unconventional sources has a downside:

■ they are all fossil fuels, so their use will continue to threaten the carbon cycle and contribute to global warming

■ extraction is costly and requires a high input of complex technology, energy and water

■ they all threaten environmental damage, from the scars of opencast mines and land subsidence to the pollution of groundwater and oil spills. Certainly, the resilience of fragile environments will be sorely tested

The last of these bullet points clearly signals social costs in the form of degraded residential environments and disrupted communities. But are there any social benefits to be offset against these costs? Possibly energy companies might invest in improving the local social infrastructure as a sweetener?

Exam tip

It is unlikely that the unconventional sources of fossil fuel will ever challenge the conventional ones.

Synoptic themes

Players in the harnessing of unconventional fossil fuels have conflicting views.

- **Exploration companies:** they have a key role to play in discovering and developing reserves. However, they will be keen to see a good financial return on their exploratory work and perhaps willing to take risks with the environment in order to achieve this.
- **Leading oil and gas TNCs:** anxious that their investments in conventional fossil fuels are not threatened by competition from these unconventional sources.
- **Governments:** some will see domestic sources of these fuels as offering a higher level of energy security, while others might wish to avoid any political fall-out led by environmental groups and affected communities.
- **Environmental groups:** well organised and very vocal in pointing out risks and potential damage to the environment. Clearly, they favour renewable energy sources.
- **Affected communities:** may well be divided between those who support exploitation of the sources (on the grounds of providing jobs and generating local income) and those who see the peace and quiet of their home areas and environmental quality as being threatened.

Exam tip

Remember that particular types of player, for example governments or affected communities, do not always share the same attitudes.

Alternatives to fossil fuels

Renewable and recyclable energy

The global drive to reduce carbon dioxide emissions must involve increasing reliance on alternative sources of 'clean' energy, so decoupling economic growth from dependence on fossil fuels. Basically, this means widening the energy mix to include substantial inputs from both renewable and recyclable energy sources.

The main sources of renewable energy today are hydro, wind, solar (mainly via photovoltaic cells) geothermal and tidal. The contribution made by these sources to national energy budgets varies from country to country. It is a simple fact of geography that not all countries have renewable energies to exploit. For example, not all countries have coasts, strongly flowing rivers or climates with either long sunshine hours or persistently strong winds. Partly because of this there are very few, if any, countries where renewables might completely replace all the energy currently derived from fossil fuels. Other factors reinforcing this include:

- the relative financial costs of using non-renewable and renewable energy sources. When oil and gas prices are low, renewables become a more expensive option
- the harnessing of renewables is not without environmental costs. Think of the drowning of river valleys to create HEP reservoirs, or the large areas of land and the offshore zone that will be covered by the required number of solar and wind farms
- while the majority of people believe that we should make greater use of renewable sources, most suddenly go off the idea when it is proposed to construct a wind or solar farm close to where they live

Another fact, unpalatable to many people, is that those countries with high levels of energy consumption will have no option but to look to nuclear energy to generate their electricity supply in a reasonably carbon-free manner. A possible plus here is that nuclear waste can be reprocessed and reused, thereby making it into a recyclable energy source.

Photovoltaic cells are now the most widely used method for generating electric power using solar cells to convert energy from the sun into an electric current that can be used to power equipment or recharge batteries.

Knowledge check 38

Why do people object to wind and solar farms being built near their homes?

The use of nuclear energy does have downsides, which include:

■ risks to do with safety (accidents) and security (terrorism)
■ the disposal of radio-active waste with an incredibly long decay life
■ the technology involved is complex and therefore its use is only an option for developed countries
■ although the operational costs are low, the costs of constructing and decommissioning power stations are high

Exam tip

Be prepared to cite an example of a nuclear power station incident, such as that at Chernobyl (Ukraine) and Fukushima (Japan) — the latter caused by an earthquake and its tsunami.

UK's changing energy mix

Figure 29 shows that when it comes to primary energy consumption in the UK, there has been a complete shift away from coal. The gap in the energy mix has been largely filled by an increased use of gas. The reliance on oil has hardly changed. Much of the oil is used by transport, while most of the gas is used to generate electricity. The forecasts made on Figure 29 suggest that the energy mix is unlikely to change much in the near future. The electricity shown in the diagram is in fact 'primary electricity' generated by renewables (hydro, wind, solar and geothermal) and recyclable (nuclear) energy.

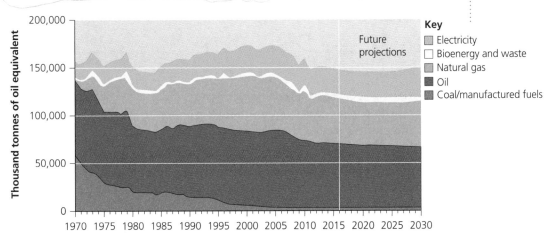

Figure 29 The UK's changing consumption of primary energy, 1970–2030

While the energy mix may have changed relatively little since 1970, the total energy consumption has declined. In short, the UK is now more efficient, both in producing energy and in using it.

Biofuels

Of all the energy sources used by humans, fuelwood perhaps has the longest history. However, while fuelwood remains important in the energy mix of some parts of the world, **biomass** has recently come into prominence with the commercial use of a number of relatively new biofuels.

The growing of **biofuel** crops is being increasingly recognised as one way of reducing both the burning of fossil fuels and carbon dioxide emissions. The most widely grown biofuel crops include wheat, corn, grasses, soy beans and sugar cane. In the UK, the two main crops are oilseed rape and sugar beet. Most of these two crops are converted into ethanol or biodiesel, which are mainly used as a vehicle fuel.

Knowledge check 39

What change in the UK economy has helped to reduce the total consumption of energy?

Biomass is organic matter used as a fuel, as for example in power stations for the generation of electricity.

But while the use of these organic fuels is to be commended on the grounds that they are 'green' energy sources, there is a serious downside to them. Simply put, each hectare of farmland used to grow energy crops means a hectare less for growing much-needed food in an increasingly hungry world. Added to this, there is still some uncertainty over how carbon-neutral biofuel crops really are.

Biofuels in Brazil

Since the 1970s, Brazil has taken steps to diversify its energy mix and improve its energy security. This drive has been spearheaded by developing the country's considerable hydro power resources. More recently, it has added biofuels to its energy portfolio. Although less than 5% of Brazil's energy comes from renewable energy sources, 90% of new passenger vehicles sold in the country have flex-fuel engines that work using any combination of petrol and ethanol. This has led to a significant reduction in the country's carbon emissions.

Large areas of central southern Brazil are now set aside for the cultivation of sugar cane and the subsequent production of ethanol. The result has been the displacement of other types of agriculture, particularly cattle rearing. The need to find replacement pastures has had a serious knock-on effect. It has resulted in the large-scale clearance of tropical rainforest in the Amazon Basin. Ironically, this deforestation nullifies the reduction in carbon dioxide emissions gained from the increasing use of ethanol.

Radical technologies to reduce carbon emissions

Finally, it is necessary to consider two rather more radical technologies. These promise to reduce carbon emissions while the world continues to meet the ever-rising demand for energy.

1 **Carbon capture and storage** involves 'capturing' the carbon dioxide released by the burning of fossil fuel, and burying it deep underground. Unfortunately, it is an expensive process because of the complex technology involved. There is also some uncertainty whether the stored carbon will stay trapped underground and that it will not slowly leak to the surface and into the atmosphere.

   Since it is widely accepted that fossil fuels will continue to provide most of the world's primary energy, development of the carbon capture and storage technology must be given a high priority, as must also the slightly different technology that 'scrubs' some of the carbon dioxide out of exhausts produced by the burning of fossil fuels.

2 **Hydrogen fuel cells** combine hydrogen and oxygen to produce electricity, heat and water. They will produce electricity as long as hydrogen is supplied; they will never lose their charge. They are a promising technology for use as a source of heat and electricity for buildings, and as a power source for electric vehicles.

   The challenge with this technology is finding a cheap and easy source of hydrogen. Although it is a simple and abundant chemical element, it does not occur naturally as a gas. It is always combined with other elements, for example with oxygen in water. Once this challenge has been met, these cells offer the real prospect of reducing carbon emissions.

Biofuel is derived directly from organic matter, such as agricultural crops, forestry or fishery products, and various forms of commercial and domestic waste. **Primary biofuels** include fuelwood, wood chips and pellets, as well as other organic matter, that are used in unprocessed form, primarily for heating, cooking and electricity generation. **Secondary biofuels** are derived from the processing of biomass and include liquid biofuels, such as ethanol and biodiesel, which can be used in motor vehicles and some industrial processes.

Exam tip

Be sure that you know the names of some biofuel crops and that they are mainly converted into fuels for motor vehicles.

A world free from the need to burn fossil fuels for energy is highly improbable. However, a world deriving much of its energy from renewable and recyclable sources, and making full use of the hydrogen fuel cell, does promise much less disturbance of the carbon cycle, its stores and fluxes.

How are the carbon and water cycles linked to the global climate system?

- The growing demand for food, fuel and other resources is threatening biological carbon stores, the water cycle and soil health.
- The degradation of both carbon and water cycles is having an adverse impact on human wellbeing.
- Global warming and climate change require co-ordinated international efforts to reduce carbon emissions, and to devise effective adaptive and mitigating strategies.

Carbon and water cycles threatened by human activity

In this section, attention focuses on three ways in which the biological carbon cycle is being disrupted by human activities. The first of these is directly by resource exploitation and associated land-use changes. The other two ways are the indirect consequences of climate change and the enhanced greenhouse effect.

Growing resource demands

The burning of fossil fuels is not the only human activity that is disturbing the biological carbon and hydrological cycles. There are others related to the growing global demand for food, fuel and other resources, all of which are the outcome of continuing global population growth and economic development.

- **Deforestation:** the clearance of forests both for their timber and for the land they occupy. In the latter case, the land is mainly cultivated to provide grazing for livestock or to produce cash crops. However, as Figure 30 shows, it is not all bad news in that there is both reforestation and afforestation under way in temperate latitudes. This is helping to offset the loss of tropical rainforest 'services', but in the case of afforestation much is taking place on what was agricultural land.
- **Grassland conversion:** temperate and tropical grasslands have also become heavily exploited by agriculture. Both grassland types have suffered as a result of overexploitation. The simple act of ploughing leads to an immediate loss of both carbon dioxide and moisture, as well as a change in runoff characteristics.
- **Urbanisation:** no land-use conversion is greater than that associated with urbanisation. Much space has already been taken over and many ecosystems completely destroyed by the insatiable demand for space needed to accommodate a rapidly rising urban population and their widening range of economic activities. Of all forms of development, none is having a more disruptive impact on the carbon and water cycles than urbanisation. Towns and cities are focal points of both GHG emissions and intense water demand.

Clearly, these changes vary individually from place to place and as a consequence so does their overall impact on carbon stores, soil health and the water cycle. In some locations, the impact is considerable; in others minimal if at all.

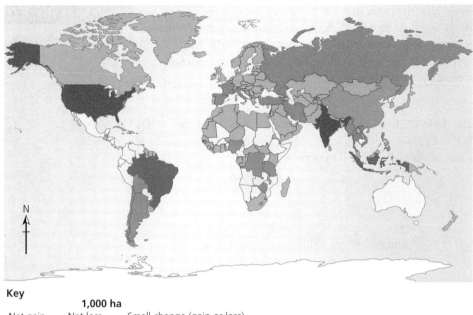

Key

1,000 ha

Net gain	Net loss	Small change (gain or loss)
■ 50–250	■ >500	■ <50
■ 250–500	■ 500–250	
■ >500	□ 250–50	□ No data

Figure 30 Annual change in forest areas, 1990–2015

Ocean acidification

Ocean acidification is very much the outcome of climate change related to the burning of fossil fuels. It represents a serious disturbance of the biological carbon cycle. The acidification is caused by the oceans being important **carbon sinks** in the carbon cycle. Up to the early nineteenth century, the average oceanic pH was 8.2. By 2015 it had fallen to 8.1. This may seem a minuscule change, but the mean values disguise the fact that there has been a larger fall in the pH of surface waters (Figure 31). Coral reefs, an important component of ocean life, stop growing when the pH is less than 7.8.

Ocean acidification involves a decrease in the pH (alkalinity) of the oceans caused by the uptake of carbon dioxide from the atmosphere.

A **carbon sink** is any natural environment (a forest, wetland or ocean) that is capable of absorbing more carbon dioxide from the atmosphere than it releases to the atmosphere. The carbon sink function is the precursor to a particular environment becoming a carbon store.

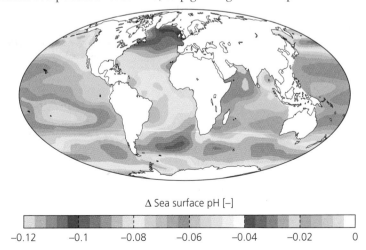

Δ Sea surface pH [–]

−0.12	−0.1	−0.08	−0.06	−0.04	−0.02	0

Figure 31 Estimated change in sea water pH between the 1700s and 1990s

So the situation is now approaching the point that there is a real risk of some marine ecosystems and their goods and services passing the critical threshold of permanent damage. In the case of coral reefs, they are also being threatened by the rise in surface water temperatures. The widespread bleaching of coral in the Great Barrier Reef of Australia is a clear indication that the threat has become a reality.

Health of forests

Like ocean acidification, the declining health of forests is also the outcome of the enhanced greenhouse effect and consequent climate change. The health of the world's forests as carbon stores is being challenged in three ways:

1 by deforestation
2 by the poleward shift of climatic belts
3 by increasing drought

The three are related in that the first and second are factors encouraging the third.

Amazon droughts

This is well illustrated by the Amazon rainforest, which acts as a giant climate regulator. Every day, it pumps 20 billion tonnes of water into the atmosphere. This is 3 billion tonnes more than the River Amazon discharges into the Atlantic Ocean. The forest's uniform humidity lowers atmospheric pressure, allowing moisture from the Atlantic to reach almost across the continent. However, since 1990, a cycle of extreme drought and flooding has been observed. Droughts in 2005 and 2010 greatly degraded much of the forest already stressed by prolonged and large-scale deforestation.

In short, the diminishing health of the tropical rainforest means that it is:

■ declining as a carbon store
■ sequestering less carbon dioxide from the atmosphere, thereby exacerbating the greenhouse effect
■ playing a diminished role in the hydrological cycle

Implications for human wellbeing

First, the point should be made that while human activities are largely responsible for the climate change resulting from the enhanced greenhouse effect, the consequent disruption of the carbon and water cycles is having a negative rebound effect on human wellbeing.

Impacts of forest loss

It is now widely understood that the impacts of deforestation are global in scale and not just confined to deforested areas. We now understand the value of forests, for example in:

■ sequestering carbon dioxide from the atmosphere
■ storing carbon
■ transferring moisture from the soil back into the atmosphere by evapotranspiration

It looks as if the Kuznets curve (Figure 32) is correct in suggesting that, as they reach higher levels of development and wealth, societies approach a tipping point when the costs of resource exploitation become fully realised and are set against the benefits of resources conservation and protection.

Knowledge check 40

What is the difference between a carbon sink and a carbon store?

Exam tip

Be clear that the health of tropical rainforests is much more threatened by deforestation and climate change than that, say, of the boreal forests.

Knowledge check 41

Why is the health of the boreal forests less threatened than that of the tropical rainforest?

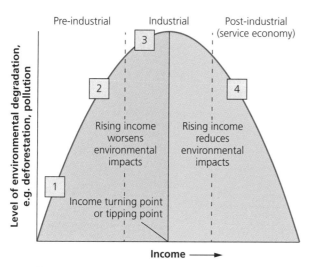

Key
1. UK pre-Industrial Revolution, remote Amazonia today, Indonesia pre-1970s
2. Indonesia today, China in the twentieth century
3. China today
4. UK today

Figure 32 The environmental Kuznets curve

UK forests

After centuries of deforestation, the forest cover of the UK had been reduced from an estimated original figure of 80% to less than 10% by the end of the nineteenth century. The Forestry Commission was set up in 1919 to remedy the country's shortage of timber. It started to plant fast-growing exotic confers, such as Sitka spruce, on the moors of Wales, the Scottish Highlands and the English Lake District and Pennines. Today 13% of the UK's land surface is now forested. In recent years, the cultivation of exotic conifers has given way to the planting of indigenous species. Today, there is much less emphasis on the commercial production of timber and more on the environmental benefits of restoring a forest cover close to the original.

So as more and more countries put the brake on deforestation and instead begin programmes of reforestation (as in the taiga), so forest loss eventually begins to have what might be seen as a positive impact.

Unfortunately, the same cannot be said for the next two changes. Their negative impacts are beginning to be understood, but as yet little remedial action is being undertaken. But will it really take, as the Kutznets curve suggests, further increases in wealth before the tide turns from exploitation to conservation?

Synoptic themes

Human wellbeing can be enhanced through a more sustainable interaction with ecosystems. The support of different players, especially governments and NGOs, is important. However, the reality is that players have different attitudes towards sustainability and on environmental issues. Attitudes are largely determined by motives. If those happen to be economic, then attitudes towards the environment may well not be sympathetic.

Impacts of rising temperatures

The rising temperatures resulting from GHG emissions are increasing both evaporation rates and the amount of water vapour. This, in turn, is impacting on:

- precipitation patterns
- river regimes
- drainage basin stores
- the cryosphere

The Arctic

The Arctic plays an important role in global climate, as its sea ice regulates evaporation and precipitation. What has happened here over the last few decades serves as a warning to the rest of the planet:

- temperatures have risen twice as fast as the global average
- there has been a considerable loss of sea ice; the North-west Passage is now open to summer navigation
- much melting of the permafrost
- carbon uptake by terrestrial plants is increasing because of a lengthening growing season
- a loss of albedo as the ice that once covered the land surface gives way to tundra, and tundra gives way to taiga. Sunlight that was previously reflected back into space by the white surface is now being increasingly absorbed by the ever darkening land surface. In other words, it is encouraging further climatic warming

In terms of human wellbeing, there have been both pluses and minuses. The warming climate is opening up previously ice-bound wilderness areas to tourism. The exploitation of mineral resources, particularly Arctic oil and gas, is becoming more feasible. However, climate warming is disrupting and perhaps annihilating traditional ways of life, for example of the fishing and hunting Inuits of North America and the Sami reindeer herders of northern Eurasia.

Synoptic themes

Although scientific understanding of the enhanced greenhouse effect is increasing, there is still much uncertainty. As a consequence, there is a commensurate degree of caution when it comes to making global projections.

Impacts of declining ocean health

The decline in ocean health caused by acidification and bleaching is resulting in changes to marine food webs. In particular, fish and crustacean stocks are both declining and changing their distributions. Such changes are being particularly felt by developing countries.

- The FAO estimates that fishing supports 500 million people, 90% of whom live in developing countries.
- Millions of fishing families depend on seafood for income as well as food.
- Seafood is also the dietary preference of some wealthier countries, notably Iceland and Japan.
- Aquaculture is on the rise, but its productivity is also being affected by declining pH values and rising temperatures.

Knowledge check 43

What is albedo?

Exam tip

Learn some key facts and figures about a case study, such as that of the Arctic, as these add weight to your answers.

Tourism is another activity under threat, particularly in those countries, for example in the Caribbean, where coral reefs, now showing signs of degradation, have traditionally attracted scuba-diving tourists. The rising sea level is yet another consequence of climate change that threatens the very survival of tourism and its coastal infrastructure, as for example in the Maldives and Seychelles. The costs of strengthening coastal defences can often exceed the financial resources of poorer coastal countries.

Responses to the risk of further global warming

An uncertain future

There is much uncertainty about the future (Figure 33), which raises many questions, particularly:

- the level of GHG emissions — will they continue to rise?
- the degree of concentration in the atmosphere — is there a limited capacity?
- the resilience of other carbon sinks — what are their capacities and could they store more?
- the degree of climate warming — how much warmer?
- feedback mechanisms such as the release of carbon from peatlands and thawing permafrost — what volumes of carbon are likely to be released?
- the rate of population growth — when, if ever, will it level off?
- the nature and rate of economic growth — will it always be so carbon-based?
- the harnessing of alternative energy sources — will fossil fuels be completely replaced?
- the possible passing of tipping points relating to such aspects as forest dieback and irreversible alterations to the thermohaline circulation — will disaster be sure to follow?

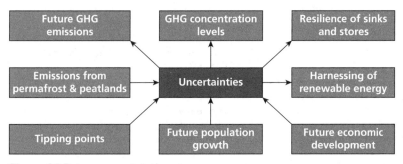

Figure 33 Future uncertainties

Synoptic themes

Figure 33 underlines the point made earlier, namely that any forecasting of global futures should be undertaken with the greatest caution. There is still so much that is unknown.

The inevitable and critical question is this: how should we react to this very real threat of further global warming? There are two different, but not incompatible, courses of action.

1 Adaptation: changing our ways of living in such a manner that we are able to cope with most, if not all, of the outcomes of global warming.

2 Mitigation: reducing or preventing GHG emissions by devising new technologies and adopting low-carbon energies (renewables and recyclables).

Exam tip

It is not all doom and gloom. There is growing evidence that some marine life is already shifting polewards to compensate for the warming seas.

Exam tip

It is worth memorising a simple diagram such as Figure 33 to help you remember points that might be covered in an exam answer on uncertainties.

Content Guidance

In the present context of global warming, adaptation is, in a sense, make do and mend — that is, living with the problem, not solving it. Mitigation, on the other hand, seeks to tackle the root cause of the problem.

Adaptation strategies for a changed climate

Table 11 sets out an evaluation of five different adaptation strategies or courses of action:

Exam tip

It is important to be certain about the difference between adaptation and mitigation.

Table 11 Costs and benefits of adaptation

Adaptation strategies	Benefits	Costs and risks
Water conservation and management	Fewer resources used, less groundwater abstraction Attitudinal change operates on a long-term basis: use more grey water (recycled water)	Efficiency and conservation cannot match increased demands for water Changing cultural habits of a large water footprint needs promotion and enforcement by governments, e.g. smart meters
Resilient agricultural systems	Higher-tech, drought-tolerant species help resistance to climate change and increase in diseases Low-tech measures and better practices generate healthier soils and may help CO_2 sequestration and water storage: selective irrigation, mulching, cover crops, crop rotation, reduced ploughing, agroforestry More 'indoor' intensive farming	More expensive technology, seeds and breeds unavailable to poor subsistence farmers without aid High energy costs from indoor and intensive farming Genetic modification is still debated but increasingly used to create resistant strains, e.g. rice and soya Growing food insecurity in many places adds pressure to find 'quick fixes'
Land-use planning	Soft management: land-use zoning, building restrictions in vulnerable flood plains and low-lying coasts Enforcing strict runoff controls and soakaways	Public antipathy Abandoning high-risk areas and land-use resettling is often unfeasible, as in megacities such as Dhaka, Bangladesh or Tokyo-Yokohaa, Japan A political 'hot potato' Needs strong governance, enforcement and compensation
Flood-risk management	Hard management traditionally used: localised flood defences, river dredging Simple changes can reduce flood risk, e.g. permeable tarmac Reduced deforestation and more afforestation upstream to absorb water and reduce downstream flood risk	Debate over funding sources, especially in times of economic austerity Land owners may demand compensation for afforestation or 'sacrificial land' kept for flooding Constant maintenance is needed in hard management, e.g. dredging; lapses of management can increase risk Ingrained culture of 'techno-centric fixes': a disbelief that technology cannot overcome natural processes
Solar radiation management	Geoengineering involves ideas and plans to deliberately intervene in the climate system to counteract global warming The proposal is to use orbiting satellites to reflect some inward radiation back into space, rather like a giant sunshade It could cool the Earth within months and be relatively cheap compared with mitigation	Untried and untested Would reduce but not eliminate the worst effects of GHGs; for example, it would not alter acidification Involves tinkering with a very complex system, which might have unintended consequences or externalities Would need to continue geoengineering for decades or centuries as there would be a rapid adjustment in the climate system if SRM stopped suddenly

The carbon cycle and energy security

1 water conservation and management
2 resilient agricultural systems
3 land-use planning
4 flood-risk management
5 solar radiation management

Four of the strategies involve a mix of soft- and hard-engineering actions. Some of those actions are low in technology and upfront costs and so, in theory, are possible options for developing countries. A change in traditional practices and customs is often required here. However, there are also actions requiring high inputs of capital and technology that only developed countries can contemplate. The whole of the solar radiation management strategy clearly falls into this category.

Mitigation and rebalancing the carbon cycle

The long-term solution to the global warming crisis lies in rebalancing the carbon cycle, particularly reducing the concentration of GHGs in the atmosphere. This requires taking actions that fall under the heading of mitigation. Table 12 sets out five possible mitigations. None is straightforward, except possibly afforestation. Successful implementation requires a society to change the way it thinks and acts. Some mitigation has a high technological tariff.

Exam tip
Be sure that you are aware of at least two of the strategies in Table 11 in terms of their benefits and costs, as well as their feasibility in different parts of the world.

Knowledge check 44
For one of the adaptation strategies in Table 11, give examples of soft- and hard-engineering actions.

Table 12 Mitigation methods applied to the UK

Methods	UK's Department of Energy and Climate Change (DECC) policies
Carbon taxation	The carbon price floor tax sets a minimum price companies have to pay to emit CO_2. It was unpopular with both industry and environmental groups and had a debateable effect on emissions. In 2015, the policy was 'frozen' Lower road taxes for low-carbon-emitting cars were scrapped in 2015 In 2015, oil and gas exploration tax relief was expanded to support fossil fuels, hence the fracking debate
Renewable switching	The relationship between the big energy providers and the government dictates the amount of switching from fossil fuels to renewables and nuclear power. Renewables (solar, wind and wave) provide intermittent electricity, while fossil fuels provide the continuous power essential for our current infrastructure The Climate Change Levy, designed in 2001 to encourage renewable energy investment and use, was cut in 2015
Energy efficiency	The Green Deal scheme encouraged energy-saving improvements to homes, such as efficient boilers and lighting, and improved insulation. It was scrapped in 2015 Energy suppliers must comply with the Energy Company Obligation scheme to deliver energy-efficient measures to householders
Afforestation	Tree planting in the UK is increasing, helping carbon sequestration. It involves the Foresty Commission, charities such as the National Trust and the Woodland Trust, landowners and local authorities. The Big Tree Plant campaign encourages communities to plant 1 million new trees, mostly in urban areas
Carbon capture and storage (CCS)	Few actual geologic CCS projects exist globally, despite its potential. Canada's Boundary Dam is the only large-scale working scheme In 2015, the UK government cancelled its investment in full-scale projects at gas- and coal-powered plants in Peterhead in Scotland and Drax in Yorkshire, respectively

Content Guidance

There are two other important points to be made about mitigation and, to some extent, about adaptation too.

1 The first is to recognise that there is a range of possible human intervention options and targets that runs from 'business as usual' (but perhaps making some adaptations) to 'aggressive mitigation' (Figure 34). RCPs (recommended concentration pathways) are four different concentrations of GHGs in the atmosphere identified by the IPCC (Inter-government Panel on Climate Change). The sobering message is that even with strong mitigation measures, there is no guarantee that even if emissions are halved by 2080 the mean global temperature will not rise by more than 2°C.

Knowledge check 45

Apart from afforestation, which of the other methods in Table 12 do you think is the most feasible?

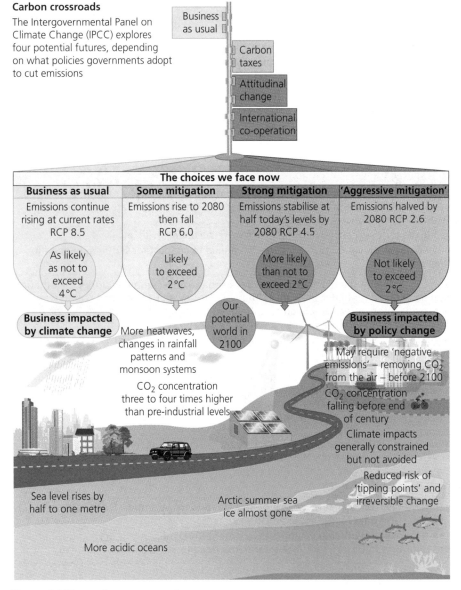

Carbon crossroads

The Intergovernmental Panel on Climate Change (IPCC) explores four potential futures, depending on what policies governments adopt to cut emissions

Business as usual

Carbon taxes

Attitudinal change

International co-operation

The choices we face now

Business as usual	Some mitigation	Strong mitigation	'Aggressive mitigation'
Emissions continue rising at current rates RCP 8.5	Emissions rise to 2080 then fall RCP 6.0	Emissions stabilise at half today's levels by 2080 RCP 4.5	Emissions halved by 2080 RCP 2.6
As likely as not to exceed 4°C	Likely to exceed 2°C	More likely than not to exceed 2°C	Not likely to exceed 2°C

Business impacted by climate change

More heatwaves, changes in rainfall patterns and monsoon systems

Our potential world in 2100

CO_2 concentration three to four times higher than pre-industrial levels

Business impacted by policy change

May require 'negative emissions' – removing CO_2 from the air – before 2100

CO_2 concentration falling before end of century

Climate impacts generally constrained but not avoided

Reduced risk of 'tipping points' and irreversible change

Sea level rises by half to one metre

Arctic summer sea ice almost gone

More acidic oceans

Figure 34 The carbon crossroads

2 The second is that if mitigation, at whatever pitch, is to have any chance of success, it not only requires concerted actions at a national level but, more critically, it requires effective international agreements. Global warming is a global problem requiring global action.

The latter point was first accepted by the Kyoto Protocol in 1997, an international agreement which aimed to cut GHG emissions by 5% by 2012. Since then, the reduction targets have been revised upwards and emissions have been reduced. It remains to be seen whether enough is being done or whether the global mitigation strategy should be made even more aggressive. It has to be said that not every country has been enthusiastic about signing up to the succession of agreements tabled since 1997. The most recent of these, the Paris Agreement of 2016, aims to keep the rise in the global temperature to less than 2°C above its pre-industrial level. The Agreement now has 140 national signatures. Among the more reluctant signatories are the three largest producers of GHGs: China, India and the USA (withdrew in 2017). Can the leopard really change its spots?

Synoptic themes

It is a sobering fact that the attitude of a large proportion of the world's population to the threat of global warming is one of indifference. TNCs may express concern, but are often found wanting when it comes to taking appropriate action. When it comes to government attitudes, those whose contributions to GHG emissions are relatively small are vociferous in drawing attention to those countries that are large contributors.

Exam tip

Remember that the four RCPs refer to the concentration of GHGs in the atmosphere, not to the rate of emission.

Knowledge check 46

Why is international agreement the key to any successful mitigation of global warming?

Exam tip

Learn the locations and dates of important IPCC meetings: Kyoto (1997), Copenhagen (2009) and Paris (2015)

Summary

- Most global carbon is locked in terrestrial stores (rocks) as part of a long-term geological cycle.
- Biological processes sequester carbon on land and in the oceans, but on a short time cycle.
- A balanced carbon cycle is important in sustaining other Earth systems, but it is being increasingly disrupted by human activities.
- Energy security is a key goal for all countries, but it needs to be achieved with much less dependence on fossil fuels.
- Economic development still relies heavily on fossil fuels as a source of energy.
- Maintaining energy pathways is a vital aspect of energy security.

- There are energy alternatives to fossil fuels, but each has its costs and potential benefits.
- Both the biological carbon and water cycles are threatened by human activities.
- The threat comes largely from the growing demand for food, fuel and other resources.
- The degradation of carbon and water cycles threatens human wellbeing, particularly in developing countries.
- Further global warming risks releasing more carbon and, as such, needs responses from different players at different scales.

Superpowers

What are superpowers and how have they changed over time?

- Some countries, and country groupings, have much greater geopolitical influence than others because of their geographical characteristics.
- Geopolitical power is dynamic, it has changed in the past and continues to change as countries rise and fall in global influence.
- Today, a number of emerging powers are important but each has different strengths and weaknesses.

Sources of geopolitical power

Defining superpowers

The power and influence of countries is very variable. The global TV news tends to be dominated by stories about the USA, China and EU countries. This is because these countries have a disproportionate amount of global influence. Geopolitical power can be thought of as a hierarchy, as shown in Figure 35.

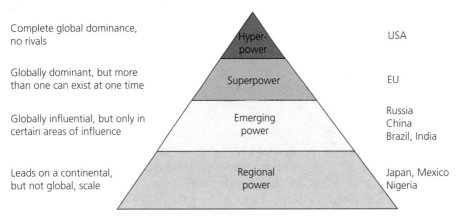

Complete global dominance, no rivals	Hyper-power	USA
Globally dominant, but more than one can exist at one time	Superpower	EU
Globally influential, but only in certain areas of influence	Emerging power	Russia China Brazil, India
Leads on a continental, but not global, scale	Regional power	Japan, Mexico Nigeria

Figure 35 The geopolitical hierarchy

Today, the USA is the only true superpower. Some view the USA as not 'just' a superpower but as a hyperpower because it is so much more powerful than other countries. The EU is hard to classify into the hierarchy. This union of 28 countries and 510 million people is a nuclear weapons power (UK, France) and the world's second largest economy after the USA. The fact that its 28 member states often disagree is a weakness in terms of global power. The EU could be further weakened when the UK leaves in 2019–2020 following the 2016 Referendum vote.

Power has a number of different sources (Table 13) and few countries 'tick all the boxes'.

Emerging powers are countries whose power is increasing; they usually have some strengths but also weaknesses in some areas in comparison with a superpower.

Geopolitical refers to the influence of geographical factors (economy, population size, military strength) on the actions of countries towards others: their foreign policy, agreements and alliances and conflicts.

A superpower is a country that can project its power and ideas globally, and influence other countries using its economic, political, military and cultural strengths.

Table 13 Sources of power

Economic	Political	Military
A large total GDP gives countries the wealth needed to be a global player	Leading, rather than following, within global organisations such as the UN, IMF and WTO	Nuclear weapons, a large navy and airforce are required to threaten or force a country's will on others
Cultural	**Demographic**	**Natural resources**
Having ideas, art, music, food and fashion that other people find appealing is a source of power	Power requires people, to support a large economy and the military	Fossil fuels, land for farming, mineral wealth and water resources increase self-sufficiency

Mechanisms of power

Table 14 shows possible ways of measuring power. The USA, EU and China are at or near the top in all columns. Other countries, such as India and Russia, do well only in some rankings.

The types of power these rankings suggest can be placed on a spectrum from hard power to soft power.

- Hard power: using military and economic influence (trade deals, **sanctions**) to force another country to act in a particular way.
- Soft power: more subtle persuasion of countries to act in particular ways, on the basis that the persuader is respected and appealing. Includes political persuasion (diplomacy) and cultural influence.

The political scientist Joseph Nye coined the term soft power. He argues that in the twenty-first century the most successful countries are those that combine hard and soft power into **smart power**.

2015/2016 data	Total GDP (US$ trillions)	Population (millions)	Active nuclear warheads	Percentage of the world's 2000 largest TNCs
USA ●	18.5	1382	1790	27
EU ●	17.1	1326	1750	20
China ●	11.4	510	440	13
Japan ●	4.7	324	260	11
India ●	2.2	210	120	3
Brazil ●	1.8	143	0	1
Russia ●	1.3	126	0	1

Table 14 Economic, demographic and military rankings

An important question is whether hard or soft power is more effective.

Sanctions are penalties applied by one country (or international organisation such as the UN) to another, such as refusal to trade with them, refusing foreign travel or banning them from taking part in international sport.

Smart power means a combination of threat and persuasion: a 'carrot and stick' approach to a country getting its own way.

Knowledge check 47

In 2017, how many member states made up the EU?

- Hard power (threats of force or direct military action) can get results but is expensive and risky.
- Others may view military action as unnecessary or illegal, so the aggressor may lose allies and moral authority (e.g. Russia's 2014 invasion of the Crimea).
- Soft power relies on a country having respected culture, values and politics, which may be enough to persuade some countries but not others.
- Soft power, applied well, is low cost and, because it is about creating alliances and friendly relations, may spread to other countries.

International rankings of soft power, such as by *Monocle* magazine, usually place the USA, UK, France and Germany top of the annual rankings, i.e. Western, liberal democracies.

Changing mechanisms

The relative importance of different forms of power has changed over time. In the past, military force and hard power were the common mechanisms for achieving and maintaining power.

In the nineteenth and early twentieth centuries the idea that power came from controlling vast land areas was important. In 1904 British geographer Halford Mackinder produced an influential **geo-strategic** location theory, called Heartland Theory (Figure 36).

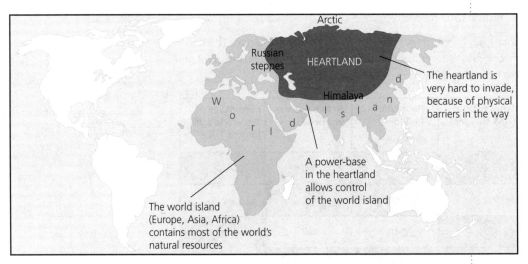

Figure 36 Heartland theory

Heartland theory was influential.
- It persuaded the USA, UK and other European countries that Russia needed to be 'contained', i.e. prevented from spreading outward by taking over new areas close by.
- It reinforced that idea that control of physical resources (land, mineral wealth) was important.

In the twenty-first century these ideas seem old-fashioned.
- Modern military technology (inter-continental ballistic missiles, drones, aircraft carriers, strike aircraft) can hit deep inside another country's territory — size is no protection.

Exam tip

Learn some data, such as in Table 14, because you need to be able to state some hard facts in the exam to back up your explanations.

Knowledge check 48

Which country has the most active nuclear warheads?

Geo-strategic refers to the policies of a country in terms of securing the resources it needs, both within its territory, nearby and globally.

Knowledge check 49

Give an example of a recent use of 'hard power'.

- Physical resources are traded internationally; there is much less need to have them domestically.
- War and conflict are generally seen as abnormal, whereas in the past they were accepted ways of gaining power.

Soft power has become more common as a way of gaining influence and maintaining power, by creating economic and political alliances. However, hard power still exists.

- In 1991 and 2003 the USA and its allies invaded Iraq, partly to secure oil supplies.
- Russia invaded Georgia in 2008 and Ukraine/Crimea in 2014, claiming to be protecting ethnic Russians.

Patterns of power

Imperial power

The period 1500 to 1950 was an imperial era. European powers (Spain, Portugal, UK, France and Germany) conquered land in the Americas, Africa and Asia and built **empires** that directly controlled territories. The development of empires relied on:

- powerful navies to transport soldiers and equipment to areas of potential conquest, and then protect sea-routes and coastlines from enemies
- large and advanced armed forces to conquer territory and then control it
- businesses, often government owned, to exploit resources in the conquered territories by mining (gold, tin) and plantation farming (rubber, tea, coffee)
- a fleet of merchant ships, protected by a navy, to transport goods back to the home country
- people from the home country to act as the government and civil service to run the colonies

Empires were maintained directly by force. Attempts by the conquered people to rebel against the colonial power were brutally suppressed. Britain had the largest empire, reaching its peak in 1920 when it controlled 24% of the world's land across all continents.

Empires ended in the period 1950–1970. European countries gave independence to their colonies. This was because the cost of maintaining empires was too high as Europe rebuilt after the Second World War. Since 1950, China has effectively acted as a colonial ruler of Tibet, brutally suppressing dissent during rebellions by Tibetans in 1959 and 2008.

Indirect control

Even during the imperial era, there was a limited attempt to control colonies using power mechanisms other than military. In British India, English culture was encouraged at least among wealthier Indians. This included English schools and language, competitive sport (cricket) and dress.

Today, no superpower or emerging power has a significant empire — although Russian-controlled parts of Georgia, Ukraine and Moldova are a mini-empire — so control of other places and people has to be indirect. These indirect mechanisms are summarised in Table 15.

An **empire** is a group of territories and their peoples ruled over by one country, usually taken by conquest. The conquered territories are usually called colonies.

Content Guidance

Table 15 Indirect mechanisms of power

Political	Military
Dominance in international decision-making within the United Nations, G7, World Trade Organisation and others. Some countries have disproportionate influence	The threat of large, powerful armed forces with global reach. Selective arms trading that provides weapons to key allies, but not enemies
Economic	**Cultural**
The use of trade deals and trade blocs to create economic alliances that create interdependence between like-minded countries	The use of global media (TV, film, music) arts, culture and global TNC brands to spread the **ideology** and values of a country through consumer culture

Indirect power became important during the **Cold War** era. The USA and USSR sought allies among other countries as part of the USA-led 'West' or USSR-led 'East'. This included:

- military alliances, e.g. USA (NATO) and the USSR (Warsaw Pact)
- foreign aid as a way to 'buy' support from emerging and developing nations
- support for corrupt and undemocratic regimes in the developing world, in return for their support for the superpower

Some geographers have argued that Western nations continue to control their ex-colonies in the developing world through an indirect mechanism called neo-colonialism, which includes:

- a debt–aid relationship: developing countries owe money for past loans to developed countries, but their poverty means they also depend on hand-outs of foreign aid
- poor terms of trade: developing countries export low value commodities (tea, copper, cocoa) but have to import expensive manufactured goods from developed countries
- the loss of their brightest and most productive people: who tend to migrate to developed countries if they can

The rise of China as an emerging power since 2000 has led to it being accused of neo-colonial actions in Africa. In addition, it is challenging the hegemony of the USA and former colonial powers (France and the UK) in Africa.

Geopolitical stability and risk

Patterns of power vary over time, and can be characterised as:

- uni-polar: one globally dominant superpower, or hyperpower
- bi-polar: two opposing superpowers, with different ideologies, but broadly equal in status
- multi-polar: many broadly equal powers, with regional influence but less global influence

Over time, patterns of power have changed (Table 16). In a uni-polar world there is one **hegemon** which is unchallenged by other countries.

Exam tip

Political, military, economic and cultural power are sometimes called the 'pillars' of superpower status. These pillars provide a useful structure for evaluating power in essay questions.

Ideology refers to a set of beliefs, ideas and values held by most people in a society. In Western countries such as the USA and Europe the dominant ideology is one of democracy, capitalism and freedom.

The **Cold War**, between 1945 and 1990, was a tense period dominated by the USA and USSR (Russia) superpowers which were broadly equal in terms of power and influence, but ideologically opposed to each other.

Knowledge check 50

When was the Cold War between the USSR and USA?

A **hegemon**, or hegemonic power, is a superpower that has mastery over all others. This includes in cultural terms, as well as economic and military ones.

Table 16 Timeline of changing polarity

British Empire 1800–1919	Inter-war period 1919–1939	USA vs USSR Cold War 1945–1990	USA globalised era 1990–2030?	Future 2030–
Uni-polar	Multi-polar	Bi-polar	Uni-polar	Bi-polar? Multi-polar?

It is interesting to consider which pattern of power is more stable, and which brings higher risk.

- A uni-polar world should be stable: there is only one 'top-dog', but the costs of being the hegemon are high and hard to sustain. The USA has been called 'the world's policeman', meaning it is involved in numerous trouble spots all at the same time.
- Bi-polar situations, such as the Cold War, involve a tense stand-off between opposing powers and might be described as high risk 'scary but stable'. During the Cold War there were occasions when the USSR and USA *almost* ended up in a 'hot' war.
- Between the First and Second World Wars the world was multi-polar with no dominant power. It could be argued this created a power vacuum allowing the rise of Nazi Germany and Imperial Japan, with no country prepared to stop them.

This has implications for the future. After 2030 the world could be bi-polar (USA and China) or it might be more multi-polar (USA, China, India, EU). This will have big implications for the sort of world we live in.

The emerging powers

Emerging powers

The global consensus is that some emerging powers will be increasingly important to global economic and political systems in the twenty-first century and the dominance of the USA will decline. The most likely rival to the USA's current hegemony is China, because:

- it has huge human resources
- its economy has grown massively since 1990, and shows few signs of slowing down
- it increasingly engages with other parts of the world, notably by investing in Africa in terms of mineral resources
- it has military ambitions to build a **blue water navy**, operating beyond its coastline

Other BRIC (Brazil, Russia, India and China) and **G20** countries could become significantly more powerful in the future. Figure 37 shows that Europe's and the USA's share of world GDP has been in decline for some time. Having declined up to 1960, China and India are now becoming increasingly significant to the global economy and that is likely to continue.

It is likely that emerging powers in the near future will:

- demand more say in global organisations such as the United Nations: there is a case for India having a permanent seat on the UN Security Council
- have more influence over global financial decision-making at the World Bank, International Monetary Fund and World Trade Organization
- play a greater role in international peacekeeping missions and disaster response, as their military capacities grow

> **Exam tip**
>
> Make sure you have a clear historical timeline about how the polarity of power has changed over time, with dates.

A **blue water navy** operates in the open ocean, whereas a green water navy has only ships that can operate close to the coast.

The **G20**, or Group of 20, is an international forum for twenty of the world's largest economies.

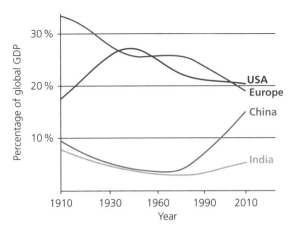

Figure 37 Shares of global GDP, 1910–2010

The BRIC countries account for 42% of global carbon dioxide emissions. This means a **global environmental governance** agreement to tackle global warming has to involve these countries. At the UN Climate Change Conference in Paris in 2015 the BRIC countries were involved in the agreement in a way they had not been when the 1997 Kyoto Protocol was signed, which only involved developed countries.

Strengths and weaknesses

Emerging countries have contrasting strengths and weakness as summarised in Table 17. Several points are worth stressing.

Table 17 Emerging power strengths and weaknesses

Emerging country	Global rank by total GDP in 2016	Key strengths	Key weaknesses
China	2	Powerful manufacturing economy Growing military power and technology	Ageing population Unwilling to engage with global problems Environmental problems
India	7	Youthful population, **demographic dividend** Global leader in IT technology	Widespread poverty Poor energy and transport infrastructure Lack of water resources
Brazil	9	Huge natural resources and farming potential Modern economic structure	Economy has boom and bust cycles Limited military strength
Russia	12	Very powerful, nuclear armed military Large oil and gas reserves	Difficult relations with the rest of the world Ageing population
Japan	3	Technologically advanced economy and global TNCs Culturally influential via technology, e.g. gaming	Ageing, declining population Very slow economic growth since 1990
Mexico	15	Advanced economy, part of NAFTA	Poor reputation for crime and corruption
Nigeria	26	Untapped natural resources Vast population and growth potential	Deep-seated poverty Internal conflict

(China, India, Brazil, Russia bracketed as BRIC)

Global environmental governance refers to international treaties and agreements that aim to reduce pollution, destruction of ecosystems and climate change.

A **demographic dividend** refers to a youthful population today (under 15) that will become a large working-age population in the future, boosting economic growth.

- Countries with ageing, or even declining, populations (Russia, Japan, some EU countries and even China) face major problems in the future in paying for increasingly costly healthcare at the same time as their workforce shrinks.
- Shortages of physical resources could derail the ambitions of some countries (India) whereas growing pollution could stall the growth of others (China).
- Countries with modern infrastructure, balanced economic sectors and good energy supplies (China, Brazil, Mexico) will do better than ones yet to develop these (India, Indonesia, Nigeria).

To be a true superpower, any emerging power will need to engage with the rest of the world and become a leader on issues such as global security, the fight against terrorism, response to disasters and environmental issues. Interestingly, this is what China has often failed to do so far.

Development theory

Theories can help explain changing patterns of power, i.e. why some countries become powerful, whereas others do not. Three theories are worth considering.

1 WW Rostow's **Modernisation Theory**. Sometimes known as the 'Take-Off model'. It suggests that economic development only begins when certain pre-conditions are met: modern infrastructure, education, banking and effective government.

2 AG Frank's **Dependency Theory**. Argues that the relationship between developed and developing countries is one of dependency: this prevents developing countries from making economic progress. Neo-colonial mechanisms and a net transfer of wealth from developing to developed world are responsible.

3 Immanuel Wallerstein's **World Systems Theory**. Does not see the world in Frank's developed versus developing world terms, but rather as a global system of core, semi-periphery and periphery nations. The semi-periphery countries are the emerging economies, some of which are emerging superpowers.

World Systems Theory is a good 'fit' for the current pattern of developed, emerging and developing countries. Modernisation Theory is useful in explaining how some countries manage to become wealthy. None of the theories are very good at identifying why some countries, but not others, become superpowers.

What are the impacts of superpowers on the global economy, political systems and the physical environment?

- Superpowers, and increasingly emerging powers, have disproportionate economic influence which also has cultural consequences.
- International decision making in relation to conflict, crises and environmental concerns is often dominated by a small number of powerful countries.
- The demand from superpowers and emerging powers for physical resources has environmental consequences and reveals contrasting attitudes.

Knowledge check 51

Roughly, what percentage of global GDP did China account for by 2010?

Exam tip

You need to know a range of strengths and weaknesses for the BRICs and the existing superpowers (EU, USA) and be able to judge which are the most/least powerful.

Knowledge check 52

Name an emerging power with an ageing population.

Superpowers and the global economy

Superpower influence

Superpowers have a disproportionate influence on the global economy. The USA, EU and Japan — which in 2016 accounted for about 60% of global GDP — are all Western capitalist economies. This means that they:

- are capitalist, i.e. people own businesses and employ workers, and make profits for themselves
- promote free trade in goods and services across borders
- are dominated by private enterprise, rather than government-owned companies
- promote wealth creation and accumulation by companies and individuals

Just after the end of the Second World War in 1945, Europe and the USA created a range of global Inter-governmental Organisations (IGOs) to promote this model, which still exist today. These IGOs are dominated by Western capitalist countries and their views (Table 18).

Free trade means international trade that is free from restrictions such as import/export taxes and quotas restricting the volume of trade.

Inter-governmental Organisations (IGOs) have countries as members, and work internationally on shared goals.

Table 18 Global IGOs and their role

World Bank (WB)	World Trade Organization (WTO)
1944 Lends money to developing and emerging economies to promote economic development This is done within a Western capitalist model The money originates from developed economies	1947 Works to remove barriers to international trade Has negotiated a sequence of global free trade agreements that have gradually removed trade taxes and quotas
International Monetary Fund (IMF)	**World Economic Forum (WEF)**
1945 Promotes global economic stability Aids economies in opening up to world trade and investment Comes to the aid of countries in economic difficulty	1971 A Swiss non-profit organisation It acts as a forum for discussion between business, politicians and IGOs It is pro-free trade and pro-TNCs

TNCs

Key drivers of the Western capitalist economic system and economic globalisation are big companies known as trans-national corporations (TNCs). These come in two flavours:

1 public TNCs: owned by shareholders; examples include Apple, Tesco, Shell and Zara

2 state-led TNCs: owned by governments; examples include Bank of China, EDF and Petronas

State-led TNCs are found in countries which do not follow the Western capitalism model, such as China and Russia. They are less democratic, and governments want the profits from business for themselves. These TNCs are often within strategic industries such as banking, oil and gas, vehicle manufacturing and the steel industry. Table 19 shows that the world's biggest TNCs are dominated by companies from the USA and EU, and state-owned companies from China. The latter tend to be much less global, operating mainly in China and a few other developing and emerging countries.

Knowledge check 53

Name the global IGO that promotes global free trade.

Exam tip

You can use acronyms such as WTO and IMF, but write out in full the first time you use them.

A **TNC**, or **trans-national corporation**, is a company that operates in more than one country.

Table 19 The Top 20 TNCs by revenue in 2016

Company	Revenue (US$ billions)	Company	Revenue (US$ billions)
Walmart	482	Berkshire	2010
State Grid*	329	McKeeson	192
CNP*	299	Samsung	177
Sinopec*	294	Glencore	170
Shell	272	ICBC*	167
Exxon Mobil	246	Daimler	165
VW	236	UHG	157
Toyota	236	CVS	153
Apple	233	EXOR	152
BP	225	GM	152

*= State-led ● = USA ● = EU ● = China ● = Japan ● = South Korea

Huge economic power rests with big TNCs:

- Apple's annual revenue is roughly the same size as the total GDP of Finland or Chile
- Walmart employs 2.3 million people worldwide
- 62% of the world's 2000 biggest companies in 2016 were from the EU, USA and Japan, with over 25% from the USA alone

Synoptic themes

TNCs are influential in a number of ways in terms of maintaining power and generating wealth.

- Their economic power influences trade patterns, and therefore the location of areas of growth because of their **foreign direct investment** (**FDI**).
- If TNCs decide to move somewhere else, for example US car companies moving out of Detriot, they can cause economic decline.
- TNCs invest heavily in new technology and **patents**: this earns them more money through new products and the **royalties** paid by other companies to use their patents.
- 90% of global patent royalties are paid to EU, US and Japanese companies.

Cultural influence

Cultural influence is an important aspect of power, linked to economic influence and the development and spread of new technology. TNC brands are key drivers of cultural globalisation and Westernisation. Westernisation is the adoption of western **culture** and values.

Knowledge check 54

Who owns many of China's largest companies?

Exam tip

Learn some data on the size and revenue of TNCs, as this will add depth to your answers.

Foreign direct investment (**FDI**) is when TNCs invest money abroad such as in building factories or opening offices.

A **patent** is the legal protection given to a new invention: other companies can use it, but only on payment of a **royalty** fee to the inventor (usually a company).

Culture is a system of shared beliefs, values and traditions including behaviour, dress, art, language, food, relationships, religion and even political views.

These include:

- individual freedom and rights, including gender equality and religious freedom
- the idea that accumulating wealth, owning property and consuming goods and services indicate a successful life
- the importance of leisure activities such as holidays, watching TV and films
- the importance of having the latest technology, and the idea that technology can solve problems
- living in a small family unit, rather than an extended family
- Westernisation, in Asia and South America, is most obvious in areas such as dress, the types of food people eat (fast-food such as McDonald's and KFC), the films they watch (Disney, 21st Century Fox) and the spread of American English as a 'global language'
- the importance of Westernisation stems from the fact that increasingly people in Asia and South America 'think and act like we do'. The desire to have access to the world's most famous global brands is a powerful force driving this process (Table 20)

Table 20 The top ten global brands in 2016

Google	Internet and media
Apple	Technology and media
Microsoft	Technology and media
AT&T	Telecoms
Facebook	Networking and media
Visa	Banking
Amazon	Retail and media
Verizon	Telecoms
McDonald's	Fast food
IBM	Technology

All of these global brands originate from the USA

Superpowers and international decision making

Global action

Superpowers and emerging powers have the ability to act globally. This is especially true of the USA, slightly less so for the EU and much less so for the BRICs. A key characteristic of a true superpower is that weaker countries look to it to act in times of crisis. This includes:

- intervening in war and conflict, especially when an internal conflict threatens to spill-out into other countries
- taking action in terms of crisis response, e.g. natural disaster, famine or a serious disease outbreak
- responding to terrorism, such as the threat from ISIS or Al Qaeda
- responding to longer-term threats, such as climate-change-induced global warming

For the USA, and to a lesser extent the EU, this expectation is a heavy responsibility and also a huge economic cost.

Synoptic themes

As a powerful country, the USA is often expected to act as a 'global policeman', sorting out problems wherever they happen to be. Many Americans do not accept this role. Interestingly China, despite its rising global power, is very reluctant to act in this way.

Examples of global action include those shown in Table 21.

The idea of **global policeman** dates back to 1942, when US President Roosevelt argued the USA, UK, Russia and China should 'police the world'.

Table 21 Global actions

2014 Ebola epidemic	2011 Libya crisis
The USA, UK and France led the crisis response in Liberia, Sierra Leone and Guinea, deploying military and medical assets	The EU, led by France and the UK, took military action against the Gaddafi regime, with the help of US military intelligence
War on Terror	2010 Haiti earthquake
Since 2001, the USA has led a global effort against Islamic terrorism in Iraq, Pakistan, Afghanistan, East Africa and the Middle East	The USA used its vast naval and air force assets to respond to this disaster with medical, food and infrastructure aid

Alliances

Even hyperpowers such as the USA, or Britain in the Imperial era, seek allies. Having like-minded friends adds to a superpower's strength.

- Allies can be 'eyes and ears' in distant parts of the world, spotting trouble as it develops.
- Allies increase the network of military assets spread around the world.
- Political and economic allies can form a large bloc, to force their agenda on the wider world.

Knowledge check 55

Today, which country is expected to act as the 'world's policeman'?

The USA has a broad global **military alliance**, which its emerging power challengers (China, Russia and India) cannot match (Figure 38). These alliances allow the USA to position powerful air and naval assets around the world.

A **military alliance** is a treaty between countries that usually involves mutual defence, i.e. if attacked, all alliance members will come to the aid of the attacked country.

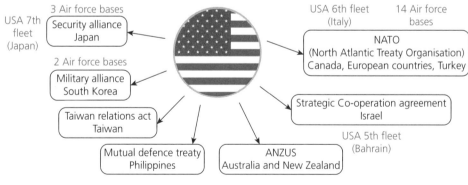

Figure 38 US military alliances and key global military assets

The USA and its military allies spent US$966 billion on their militaries in 2015, or 58% of global military spending.

As well as being tied together economically, superpowers are tied by economic alliances. This is achieved by **free-trade agreements**.

A **free-trade agreement** allows for tax, tariff and quota-free trade between member countries in goods and/ or services.

These include:

- the EU: between 28 member states
- NAFTA: between the USA, Mexico and Canada
- ASEAN: between 10 south-east Asian countries including Taiwan, the Philippines and Indonesia

The overlap between economic and military alliances creates interdependence in terms of geostrategy. Economic prosperity requires geopolitical stability (wars are bad for trade), which is ensured by military alliances.

Synoptic themes

Most of the world's powerful inter-governmental organisations (IGOs) such as the United Nations, World Trade Organization and EU were set up by Western countries in the 1940s and 1950s. Their actions frequently reflect Western attitudes to trade, capitalism, political freedom and the environment. They may not reflect the attitudes of emerging powers such as China or Russia.

The United Nations

The UN (United Nations) was set up in 1945. With other global IGOs, it was part of an attempt to create a new world order of peace, prosperity and stability and avoid further world wars.

The most powerful decision-making body within the UN is the Security Council. It makes decisions on issues such as:

- taking military action against countries seen to be breaking international law or persecuting people
- applying economic or diplomatic sanctions to countries, to try to force them to change their behaviour

The Security Council's five permanent members tend to act as two blocs, as shown in Figure 39, which gives the 'Western' powers a 3:2 advantage.

The USA, France and UK (all NATO members) tend to vote together

Russia and China often vote the same way, or abstain from some votes

Figure 39 The UN Security Council

The UN is important in other ways.

- The International Court of Justice upholds international law; its legal framework is a Western one, reflecting the fact that the UN was set up by the USA and European powers.
- Peacekeeping missions can be set up by the UN, sourcing armed forces from member states. These have had some success at ending or preventing conflict, e.g. the Bosnian conflict in the 1990s.

- The UN Framework Convention on Climate Change (UNFCCC) and its scientific advisory panel the **Inter-governmental Panel on Climate Change (IPCC)** are important in informing the debate on global warming, and thus international agreements such as the COP21 agreement in Paris in 2015 where many countries pledged to reduce carbon dioxide emissions.

> The **IPCC (Inter-governmental Panel on Climate Change)** is a group of scientists that reports on global warming roughly once every 5 years.

Superpowers and the environment

Resource demands

Global environmental governance is disproportionately influenced by superpowers. This is most obvious when it comes to global warming. As Figure 40 shows, any attempt to reduce greenhouse gas emissions will fail unless big emitters agree, because they account for such a large percentage of global emissions.

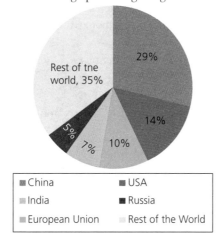

Figure 40 Global carbon dioxide emissions in 2015

- The USA and China have been reluctant to set emissions reduction targets, whereas the EU has often led in this regard.
- EU and US emissions are static or falling (because of greater efficiency and some green policies) but in China emissions are still rising.

Key questions for the next 20 years:

- What will the food, water, energy, mineral and other resource demands of emerging India, Brazil and China be as those countries get wealthier?
- Can the world's resource base provide for these emerging powers, if people attain a similar level of wealth to the EU and USA today?

Energy demand is a useful example. Projections to 2040 estimate a 40–50% increase compared with 2010. Almost all of this will come from emerging and developing countries, mostly India and China. Much of the growth is likely to be in the form of fossil fuel coal, gas and oil — meaning rising carbon dioxide emissions.

- In India, demand for food and water, as that country reduces poverty, look unsustainable by 2030 as even today India struggles with adequate water supply.
- In China, demands for cars, bigger houses and consumer goods will suck in global energy and mineral resources and could lead to rising resource prices and, potentially, shortages.

Continued economic development in emerging powers is also likely to lead to local **environmental degradation**. This will translate into health problems especially in densely populated cities.

Synoptic themes

It is important to recognise that just as attitudes to issues such as trade and globalisation differ between countries, so do attitudes to the environment. The EU has shown itself willing to act to reduce the global warming threat, but this is less true of the USA and even less so of the emerging powers (China, Russia), which tend to prioritise economic development over environmental protection.

Environmental governance

Just as the world looks to superpowers to act as 'global policemen', many people would look to the same countries to show leadership on environmental issues such as carbon emissions. Opinion on this issue is very divided, with some superpowers more willing to act to try and reach global agreements than others (Figure 41).

- China's focus is largely on economic development not environmental issues.
- In the USA concern is quite low, at 45%. There is a long-standing 'climate scepticism' in the USA.
- Europeans are more concerned. Europe has been the most willing to act to try and reduce emissions since 1990.

The very high level of concern in Africa and Latin America is interesting. Both regions have little impact on global warming as their emissions are low. They could be severely affected by climate change as both have many farmers that depend directly on rainfall for water supply, and crops for food.

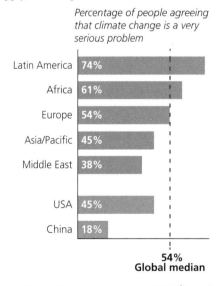

Figure 41 Global attitudes to climate change, 2015 (Pew Research Centre)

There are some reasons to be positive about **environmental governance**:

- Brazil has dramatically slowed forest loss and expanded protected areas since 2005
- China has become the world's biggest investor in renewable wind power and solar power and has cut back on coal burning

Environmental degradation means reductions in water quality, air quality, soil health and biodiversity caused by high levels of pollution, deforestation and urbanisation.

Knowledge check 57

In 2015, which single country was the world's largest emitter of carbon dioxide?

Exam tip

Be careful when discussing China. With per capita income in 2017 of around US$8,000, it is still an emerging economy not a fully developed one.

Environmental governance means the decisions taken to protect and conserve the environment, by enacting laws, policing and monitoring pollution and protected areas.

At the Paris climate summit (COP21) in 2015 all countries did agree on emissions reductions. China, still focused on economic development, agreed to reduce emissions after 2030.

Emerging demand

Over the next 30 or 40 years resource demand in the USA and EU is likely to remain static. Most people are already wealthy and their demand for additional resources will be met by increasingly efficient use of existing resources.

In emerging powers, this is not the case. Pressure on resources has a number of causes:

- increasing population, especially in India, Indonesia and Brazil
- increased wealth: the global middle class (people earning US$10–100 per day) is expected to increase from 2 billion in 2012 to a staggering 5 billion by 2030

These people will need more 'stuff' and that may be problematic (Table 22).

Table 22 Resource demands

Rare earths	Oil
80–90% of global rare earth production is in China. This raises the possibility of shortages due to resource nationalism	In 2015 the USA used 19 million barrels of oil per day, China 12 million and India 4 million. What if Indian and Chinese demand reached USA levels?
Food	**Water**
As China and India develop there will be increased demand for staple grains (wheat, rice). Demand for meat, dairy products and sugar will also rise as these countries transition to 'Western' diets	In the USA and EU washing machines, dishwashers, a daily bath/shower and swimming pools are common. This is not of true emerging countries, but vast additional water supplies will be needed if it becomes true

Increased demand is likely to have two consequences:

1 the price of key resources rises as higher demand puts pressure on supply
2 availability of resources, especially non-renewable ones, falls as some supplies are used up

In addition the rise of middle-class consumption will affect the physical environment:

- more mining, oil drilling and deforestation in the quest to access raw materials
- increased carbon emissions from higher energy consumption and more factories
- problems disposing of consumer waste in landfill sites and incinerators
- more use of water, and therefore more polluted waste water

What spheres of influence are contested by superpowers and what are the implications of this?

- Tensions can arise between superpowers and emerging powers over resources, trade and geographical spheres of influence.
- Ties between emerging powers and the developing world bring new opportunities, but could also stoke existing tensions.
- The EU and USA face challenges in terms of maintaining their global influence in an increasingly uncertain world.

Exam tip
You need to know a range of reasons why attitudes to environmental issues vary around the world.

Rare earths are a group of elements widely used in electronic, medical and laser devices. Scandium, Yttrium and Terbium are examples.

Resource nationalism is when a country keeps domestically produced resources for itself, rather than trading them internationally.

Non-renewable resources have a finite amount, or stock, so can run out. This includes fossil fuels and mineral/metal ores.

Knowledge check 58
What is the range of daily earnings in US$ that defines 'middle class'?

Contested spheres of influence

Physical resources

Superpowers and emerging powers need physical resources, especially fossil fuels, minerals and ores. Some have these domestically but in many cases they must be obtained through international trade. This can mean:

- buying resources at high prices, e.g. in 2008 crude oil was priced at US$140 per barrel
- trading with unfriendly regimes, or ones that are politically unstable, e.g. Iranian and Iraqi oil
- during conflict, trade routes and therefore supply is blocked

These factors increase the advantage of claiming new territory and its resources. In some cases tensions can arise as countries attempt to acquire natural resources, but their ownership is disputed. This can be done in several ways:

- invasion and conquest of another country's territory, which is rare
- claiming offshore, undersea resources by extending a country's **exclusive economic zone** (EEZ), which is more common

There are examples of both approaches (Table 23).

Table 23 Gaining new territory

Russian annexation of Crimea in 2014	Arctic oil and gas resources
Russia invaded and took Crimea (part of Ukraine) by force in 2014 A key reason for doing this was to gain total control of the Russian naval base at Sevastopol in Crimea — home to Russia's Black Sea Fleet The base was leased to Russia in 1997, but not owned by Russia Russia fears that if Ukraine joins the EU and/or NATO this strategic base could be lost Fearing the loss of land and a port, both physical resources, Russia acted	Huge oil and gas reserves may exist under the Arctic Ocean This area is beyond the EEZ of Canada, USA, Russia and Denmark All of these countries have claimed EEZ extensions, which are disputed by others, and lodged these with the UN (which ultimately rules on them) Since 2007, military patrols and activity have increased in the Arctic as each country shows it is interested in the area, and willing to defend its claims

The **exclusive economic zone** (EEZ) extends 200 nautical miles offshore from a country's coast, and includes all resources in and under the sea. In some circumstances its size can be extended.

Any attempt to drill for oil and gas in the Arctic could become a source of diplomatic if not actual conflict. In addition, the risks of environmental disaster from oil spills is high in one of the few remaining pristine ecosystems on the planet also with a large indigenous population, i.e. the Inuit.

Synoptic themes

Currently no natural resources are exploited in Antarctica, and few in the Arctic, but in the future this may change if some countries believe they should be exploited. The attitudes of countries may change if resources are depleted elsewhere leaving only these protected places as sources of minerals and fossil fuels.

Intellectual property

Human resources are a key element of power. This is especially the case with regard to new inventions and discoveries such as:

- new military technology, used for defence or attack
- inventions and new products that could bring riches

Knowledge check 59

Which are the two most powerful countries that have claims to some of the Arctic sea bed?

Exam tip

Make sure you can accurately locate the superpowers and emerging powers on a world map.

Most inventions are made by government organisations or TNCs through research and development (R&D).

To prevent new inventions being copied illegally, they are protected by an international system of **intellectual property (IP)**. Without this:

- TNCs would be reluctant to invest in R&D, because they would gain little profit from inventions that were immediately copied
- countries would be reluctant to trade, because their IP would fall into the hands of others who would steal it

IP has economic value. Royalty fees alone amount to US$150–200 billion annually, with 80% going to the USA, Japan and western Europe. Intellectual property theft, counterfeiting and industrial espionage can strain trade relationships, causing problems. It has been estimated that counterfeit goods sales account for 5–8% of China's GDP. Chinese car companies have copied car designs from BMW and Mercedes, and iPhones are widely **counterfeited**.

- TNCs may limit investment in China if they fear IP theft.
- Total losses worldwide are probably US$400–600 billion annually.
- Trade deals with countries such as China are made much harder by its failure to tackle IP theft.
- Counterfeit goods are often unsafe, putting consumers at risk.

Political spheres

The concept of a **sphere of influence** is useful in terms of tensions between superpowers and emerging powers over territory and physical resources. Table 24 shows the USA and its global allies. It includes a summary of regions where emerging power spheres of influence overlap with traditional US spheres.

Intellectual property (IP) includes Trademark ™, copyright © and patent protection (for physical or system inventions) and a system of royalty payments for the rights to use IP developed by someone else.

Counterfeiting means copying someone else's trademarked, branded designs — such as expensive handbags, jeans or mobile phones.

A **sphere of influence** is an area or territory, beyond a country's national borders, over which it feels it should have power but without having any formal authority there.

Table 24 Overlapping spheres of influence

1	Eastern Europe	Eastern European countries joining the EU, and moves by Georgia and Ukraine to do so, angered Russia, leading to the Russian invasions of parts of Georgia in 2008 and Ukraine in 2014, as well as a build-up of NATO armed forces in the Baltic States
2	Middle East & Central Asia	Since 2011, Russia has been an active ally of Syria, helping the Syrian government fight rebel forces and ISIS. Russia supports Iran, an enemy of US allies Israel and Saudi Arabia. Russia's increasing involvement in the Middle East makes an already difficult region even more complex
3	East China Sea	Strained relations between North Korea (a Chinese ally) and South Korea (a US ally), as North Korea works to become a nuclear power. China sees South Korea and Japan (US allies) as economic competitors. All countries have ongoing disputes over islands in the sea
4	South China Sea	Numerous disputed islands, claimed by China and US allies the Philippines and Taiwan. China has aggressively pursued a policy of island settlement and artificial island building — then adding military facilities
5	Central America	China has shown increasing interest in funding alternative routes to the Panama Canal between the Atlantic and Pacific. This is an area of traditional US hegemony

The South China Sea is a very tense region. China's 'Nine-Dashed Line' and 'First and Second Island Chain' policies force it to try and control a large area of the ocean south and east of China. The USA has considered this its sphere since the end of the Second World War. The situations in Ukraine, Georgia and Syria have created refugee crises — in Syria on a huge scale from 2011 to 2017. This shows there are implications for people of contested spheres.

Changing relationships

Developing countries

Low-income countries could have new relationships with emerging powers. An example is China's interest in Sub-Saharan Africa, the world's least developed region. China's interest is based on exploiting Africa's abundant and undeveloped physical resources:

- copper ore in Zambia
- crude oil in Angola, Sudan and Chad
- coltan (the ore of niobium and tantalum used in mobile phones) from the DRC

This new relationship has pros and cons (Table 25).

Table 25 China in Africa: opportunities and challenges

Opportunities	Challenges
China–Africa relations are based on trade, not ex-colonial ties Chinese mines and factories bring jobs and raise incomes and GDP In order to develop mining and factory investment, China has invested huge sums in HEP, railways, ports and roads — which can be used more widely China–Africa trade was worth US$200 billion in 2016, a huge sum for a developing region	Countries without natural resources China wants are left out Many jobs are actually done by Chinese migrant labour who number over 1 million Mining and oil exploitation risks causing deforestation, oil spills and water pollution Cheap Chinese imported goods have undercut some local African producers, especially of textiles Africa's economic model is still cheap raw material exports, and expensive manufactured imports

Increasingly, China depends on Africa's raw materials and Africa relies on investment from China. This **interdependence** may benefit both, but a slow-down in China's economy would also mean a slow-down in Africa's.

Synoptic themes

If developing countries align themselves economically and politically with emerging countries such as India, China and Russia this could have significant impacts on world trade patterns and geopolitical alliances. So far, only China has really achieved this in Africa.

Asian tensions

India and China represent 36% of the world's population, 18% of global GDP and 32% of global CO_2 emissions. Their rising economic importance to the world cannot be denied. Both are members of the G20, which is an increasingly important global grouping. The older G8 set up in 1975 consists of indebted developed countries, whereas the G20 includes cash-rich investor countries.

Knowledge check 60

Where did Russia invade and occupy in 2014?

Exam tip

You need a range of examples to illustrate different geographical locations contested by powerful countries.

Interdependence exists when one country or region relies, to a large degree, on another to ensure its economic prosperity.

Exam tip

Make sure you can evaluate the costs and benefits of Chinese investment in Africa.

China and India relations are interesting.

- They are ideological rivals: India is the world's largest democracy, whereas China is a communist dictatorship.
- They share a border, but parts are disputed (Arunachal Pradesh, Tawang, Aksai Chin), which led to conflict in 1962, 1967 and 1987.
- China has created a strong economic alliance with Pakistan focused on the US$54 billion Chinese investment in CPEC (China–Pakistan Economic Corridor), but Pakistan and India have tense, often antagonistic relations.
- China has the upper-hand in terms of economics, as India has a large **trade deficit** with China.

Increasingly, India and China are rivals in outer space. Both have advanced space programmes. The rocket technology from this also helps develop their nuclear missile technology. Both have an aircraft carrier, and both are building more — demonstrating they have regional if not global, naval ambitions.

Middle East tensions

The world economy runs on crude oil. The Middle East contains 60% of proven oil reserves. This is why no superpower or emerging power can ignore the Middle East.

The Middle East is an area of tension and conflict for a number of reasons.

- Most Muslim countries are hostile to the Jewish state of Israel: Iran has vowed to destroy it, but the USA is a key ally of Israel.
- Religious differences between Sunni (Saudi Arabia, Syria, Turkey) and Shia (Iran, Iraq, Lebanon) branches of the Muslim religion are a source of conflict between and sometimes within countries.
- Since 2011, the rise of the extremist group Islamic State (ISIS) in Iraq and Syria has created war, terrorism and a refugee crisis.
- The Kurdish people (in Iran, Iraq, Syria and Turkey) are demanding their own state.
- Since 2015 a civil war has raged in Yemen, which has involved Saudi Arabia directly and the USA indirectly.

The complex web of alliances and geopolitical relations within Middle Eastern countries is a major ongoing challenge to stability. Russia, and to a lesser extent China, tend to support Iran within the region. The USA and EU lean towards Saudi Arabia. The Saudis and Iranians both see themselves as regional leaders, but relations between them are very poor.

Synoptic themes

Globally, there are perhaps three contrasting cultural ideologies. Western capitalism (EU, North and South America), the Muslim world (Middle East, North Africa) and Asian. Attitudes to religion, trade, social relations, women, sexuality and the environment differ in all three. This means that geopolitical relationships between them are not always easy.

A **trade deficit** exists when a country imports from another country more than it exports to that country.

Knowledge check 61

Which opposing political systems exist in India and China?

Knowledge check 62

Which two Middle Eastern countries are rivals for regional leadership there?

Content Guidance

Existing superpower challenges

Declining USA and EU?

Since the Global Financial Crisis in 2007–2008, the EU and USA have slowly rebuilt their damaged economies. The crisis caused government debt levels to increase sharply as money was borrowed to:

- re-finance banks and other businesses facing collapse
- pay social service costs, such as unemployment benefits
- pay for new infrastructure (roads, bridges) in an effort to stimulate economic growth

By 2016 debt levels had reached 90% of annual GDP in the UK, 75% in the USA and 214% in Japan. High debt levels, in the long term, may slow down future economic growth.

Debts levels are pushed up by high social costs (Table 26).

Table 26 Social costs

Structural unemployment	Economic restructuring	Ageing and care
Loss of manufacturing jobs to emerging economies through globalisation This has led to a pool of middle-aged, low skilled, male workers without jobs Many rely on social security payments from government	The global shift to Asia has created deindustrialisation in the EU and USA There are high costs linked to regenerating former industrial areas In addition, the workforce needs retraining and re-skilling in tertiary sector jobs	Rising life expectancy and low fertility rates mean an ageing population Care home, nursing care and pension costs are all rising This has to be paid for by a shrinking working-age population in many EU countries

High debt levels, **economic restructuring** and high social costs represent an opportunity for India and China. The two emerging powers have a chance to pull level with the USA and EU because of the ongoing and long-term nature of these economic and social problems.

Superpower costs

The USA spends 3.3% of its GDP (US$596 billion in 2015) on defence, i.e. hard power. The UK spends 0.7% of its GDP (US$18.7 billion in 2015) on development assistance (foreign aid), seeing this is a key part of its soft power.

Faced with rising healthcare and ageing costs, it is easy to question this spending on military power and space exploration. Figure 42 shows the USA's government budget for 2016:

- defence takes up a very large slice, at about 15% of all spending
- **intelligence services** alone cost about US$80 billion annually
- spending by NASA on space exploration totalled US$18.5 billion in 2016
- each of the USA's ten planned Gerald R Ford-class aircraft carriers will cost US$10.4 billion
- simply to test-fire an unarmed Tomahawk cruise missile costs US$1.5 million

The UK, France and USA also spend large sums of money on nuclear missile technology and civilian nuclear power research. Both of these can be questioned.

The **Global Financial Crisis** was a stock-market crash and a series of bank failures, that in turn led to a global recession, business closures and rising unemployment.

Economic restructuring means the shift from manufacturing (secondary) industry to services (tertiary).

Knowledge check 63

Why are social care and pensions costs rising rapidly in the EU?

Exam tip

The EU and USA both have problems, but be careful not to dismiss them. China has a lot of catching up to do despite these problems!

Intelligence services (MI5, the CIA) gather information on a country's enemies, which includes spying on them.

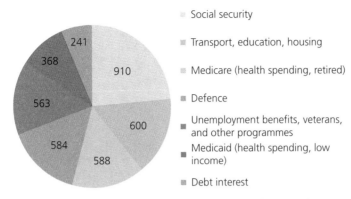

Figure 42 The USA Federal Budget in 2016 (US$ billions)

In order to be a truly global superpower, the USA must spend these sums of money. However, the money could be spent in other ways:

- about 13% of Americans live in poverty (living on less than US$12,000 per year)
- about 60,000 road and rail bridges in the USA need to be repaired
- the over 65s in the USA made up 15% of the population in 2016, this will rise to 20% by 2030

In the EU, the consequences of the Global Financial Crisis in 2007–2008 have meant government budget cut-backs, especially to defence. Russian aggression in Ukraine, the Islamic State in the Middle East and China's increasing militarisation have not so far been met with increased EU or USA military spending.

Global power in 2030 and 2050

The future balance of superpowers cannot be known. Future outcomes are just best guesses based on extrapolating past and current trends, especially total GDP levels and population.

Three possible scenarios are shown in Table 27.

Table 27 Three possible scenarios for the future balance of superpowers

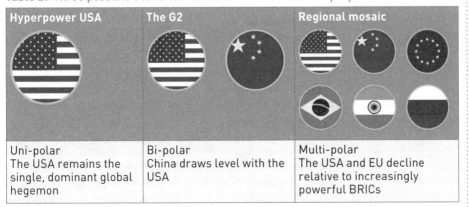

Hyperpower USA	The G2	Regional mosaic
Uni-polar The USA remains the single, dominant global hegemon	Bi-polar China draws level with the USA	Multi-polar The USA and EU decline relative to increasingly powerful BRICs

> **Knowledge check 64**
>
> Which type of government spending amounts to 0.7% of UK GDP?

By 2030:

- A similar world to today, but the Chinese economy is likely to be similar in size to that of the USA.
- Per capita incomes in China will be lower than the USA, and China will still be in the process of becoming a fully developed country.
- China is unlikely to be a global political leader by 2030.

By 2050:

- Potentially a very different world with China and India both powerful economically and militarily (and potential rivals).
- The USA could have similar levels of power and influence to India and China.

Synoptic themes

There are many unknown quantities that increase uncertainty over future superpower structures.

- Post-Brexit, and faced with a sluggish economy and huge debts, what is the future of the EU? It may stagnate as the Japanese economy has done since the mid-1990s, or renew itself and grow.
- Russia, with its oil and gas reserves and huge military arsenal (including nuclear weapons), will remain important, but is an unlikely global leader.
- The EU, Russia and even China all face the prospects of rapidly ageing populations that may diminish their status.

Exam tip

You need to be able to discuss a number of future scenarios, but always include a judgement about their uncertainty.

Summary

- Superpowers can be defined using a range of criteria to judge their status, including military, political, economic, demographic and cultural influence.
- Superpowers and emerging powers use both hard- and soft-power mechanisms to influence others, with soft power usually being seen as more important today.
- Patterns of power change over time, between uni-, bi- and multi-polar. The current uni-polar situation with the USA as hegemon replaced the bi-polar Cold War in 1990.
- There are half a dozen emerging powers, including the BRICs, but all have different strengths and weaknesses and do not yet rival the USA.
- The global economy, globalisation and TNCs are all important to superpower status and have been shaped by superpowers.

- Superpowers play a crucial role in global governance and international action, responding to disasters and sometimes working to protect the global environment — but they also have huge demand for natural resources.
- Political tensions, and even conflict, can arise when the spheres of influence of superpowers overlap.
- Emerging powers, such as China, may forge a different relationship with the developing world that contrasts with the colonial and neocolonial relationship of the past.
- The near future represents a challenge to the USA and EU as both have economic problems, but the future pattern of superpowers is very uncertain.

Questions & Answers

■ Assessment overview

In this section of the book, questions for each of the content areas are given for the Paper 1 and Paper 2 A-level examinations. The style of questions used in the exam has been replicated. There are some shorter answer questions and some extended writing questions. On the A-level exam papers most of the questions you will encounter are extended writing or essay questions.

Questions worth 6 or more marks require you to:
■ make connections between different parts of the subject content
■ provide detailed explanations
■ use examples and case studies to add geographical place detail
■ back up your explanations with evidence

It is worth thinking about the meaning of the command word you will encounter at A-level. The command words are given in the table below, by increasing level of demand. Higher demand command words require higher level thinking skills that include the ability to evaluate, draw conclusions and make judgements that are supported by evidence and make logical sense.

	Command word	Meaning	Marks
Increasing demand	Draw/plot/ complete	Add information to correctly finish a graph, map, diagram or statistical test	1–4 marks
	Suggest	For an unfamiliar scenario, write a reasoned explanation of how or why something may occur. A suggested explanation requires justification/exemplification of a point that has been identified	3 or 4 marks
	Explain	Provide a reasoned explanation of how or why something occurs. An explanation requires understanding to be demonstrated through the justification or exemplification of points that have been identified	3, 4, 6 or 8 marks
	Assess	Use evidence to determine the relative significance of something. Give balanced consideration to all factors and identify which are the most important	12 marks
	Evaluate	Measure the value or success of something and ultimately provide a balanced and substantiated judgement/ conclusion. Review information and then bring it together to form a conclusion, drawing on evidence such as strengths, weaknesses, alternatives and relevant data	20 marks

The structure of A-level Papers 1 and 2 is given below, including the questions covered by this Student Guide and those questions which are covered in accompanying Student Guides.

Paper 1

For **Paper 1**, which lasts 2 hours and 15 minutes and is worth a total of 105 marks, equivalent to 30% of the A-level qualification, the breakdown of the questions is shown in the table below.

Section of Paper 1	Total marks	Typical question sequence
Section A: Tectonic processes and hazards	16 marks	4 and 12 marks
Section B: Landscape systems, processes and change (either Coastal landscapes and change OR Glaciated landscapes and change)	40 marks	6, 6, 8 and 20 marks
Section C: The water cycle and water insecurity & The carbon cycle and energy security	49 marks	3, 6, 8, 12 and 20 marks

Paper 2

For **Paper 2**, which also lasts 2 hours and 15 minutes and is worth a total of 105 marks, equivalent to 30% of the A-level qualification, the breakdown of the questions is shown in the table below.

Section of Paper 2	Total marks	Typical question sequence
Section A: Globalisation/ Superpowers	32 marks (16 marks each)	4 and 12 marks
Section B: Shaping places (either Regenerating places OR Diverse places)	35 marks	3, 6, 6 and 20 marks
Section C: Global development and connections (Health, human rights and intervention & Migration, identity and sovereignty)	38 marks	3, 1, 6, 8 and 20 marks

The sections that follow are each structured as follows:

- sample questions in the style of the examination
- levels-based mark schemes for extended questions (6 marks and over) in the style of the examination
- example student answers at an upper level of performance
- examiner's commentary on each of the above

Study the descriptions given after each question carefully to understand the requirements necessary to achieve a high mark. You should also read the commentary with the mark schemes to understand why credit has or has not been awarded. In all cases, actual marks are indicated.

Questions

A selection of questions that are representative of the ones you will encounter in A-level Paper 1 and Paper 2 are given in this section.

Water and carbon cycle questions

Question 1

(a) Study Figure 1. Suggest **one** reason for the trend in global methane atmospheric concentration   (3 marks)

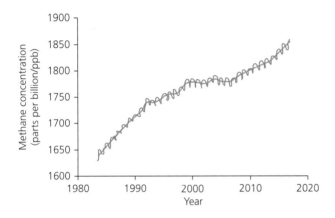

Figure 1 Global methane atmospheric concentration 1984–2016

ⓔ This is a data stimulus question. The first task is to recognise the upward trend on Figure 1, and the fact that a steep increase paused around 2000 but resumed after 2008. The question demands **one** reason. This means identifying a reason for increased methane concentrations and explaining it with two further extended points. You cannot name multiple reasons such as an increase in cattle farming and an increase in methane emission from landfill. Stick with the first reason and add additional detail.

> **Student answer**
>
> The trend in methane levels is a steep rise from 1625 ppb in 1984 to 1850 ppb by 2015, including a slower growth phase 2000–2008. The main cause of this is agriculture and especially the expansion of cattle farming. It is released by the growing number of cattle needed to meet demand for beef in emerging countries. Expanded cattle ranches often replace carbon-sequestering forests with methane-emitting cattle.

ⓔ **3/3 marks awarded**. The first sentence does not score marks because it is a description, however it does provide a focus for the explanation that follows. The one reason given — agriculture — is expanded on in terms of cattle farming, beef demand and replacing forest with ranches. The last sentence shows a good understanding of the carbon cycle.

Questions & Answers

(b) Explain the role of the oceans in the carbon cycle. (6 marks)

🄔 This is a levels marked question that requires an in-depth explanation of one part of the carbon cycle. It might be tempting to discuss other parts of the cycle, but this will not gain marks unless there is a link to the oceans. Focus on the oceans and link the ocean to other relevant parts of the cycle such as the atmosphere and geological stores. This question is quite a conceptual one that demands good use of carbon cycle terminology, i.e. you need to have revised the physical processes in depth. It is much less about 'place' because it is focused on a cycle. These 6-mark 'explain' questions in both A-level Units 1 and 2 are marked using the following levels mark scheme.

Level 1	1–2 marks	Demonstrates isolated elements of geographical knowledge and understanding, some of which may be inaccurate or irrelevant Understanding addresses a narrow range of geographical ideas, which lack detail
Level 2	3–4 marks	Demonstrates geographical knowledge and understanding, which is mostly relevant and may include some inaccuracies Understanding addresses a range of geographical ideas, which are not fully detailed and/or developed
Level 3	5–6 marks	Demonstrates accurate and relevant geographical knowledge and understanding throughout Understanding addresses a broad range of geographical ideas, which are detailed and fully developed

Student answer

The oceans contain about 38,000 gigatonnes of carbon, making them Earth's largest carbon store. Carbon is stored as dissolved CO_2 in water, or stored in algae, plants and coral. The biological pump sequesters carbon from the atmosphere through the growth of phytoplankton (photosynthesis). These form the basis of the ocean food web. Passed along the food web, carbon is returned to the atmosphere by biological decay. The biological pump takes place on a timescale of hours to years and the flux between atmosphere and ocean is 11 gigatonnes per year. Only a small proportion of carbon enters the carbon pump. This is when dead organic material, e.g. shells and dead phytoplankton, sinks to the ocean floor and becomes sediment that will eventually become carbonate rocks like limestone (geological carbon store), although on timescales of millions of years. Within the oceans, the physical pump, in the form of ocean currents and the thermohaline circulation, moves carbon vertically and horizontally. The size of the ocean carbon store makes it very important, as it has the capacity to store excess carbon produced by human activities.

⊜ 6/6 marks awarded. The strength of this answer is that it uses the correct terminology of the carbon cycle, accurately. The simplest part of the oceanic carbon cycle is phytoplankton taking in atmospheric carbon during photosynthesis. The student goes beyond that to explain the role of the carbonate and physical pumps, not just the biological pump. The answer shows understanding of carbon stores and fluxes, as well as the fact that these operate on different timescales. Carbon in the oceans is linked to atmospheric and geological stores, but the focus of the answer remains on oceanic carbon. Notice that some data values are used. These are very useful in showing depth of understanding.

Question 2

(a) Study Figure 2. Explain **one** reason why some European countries will have high levels of water stress by 2040.

(3 marks)

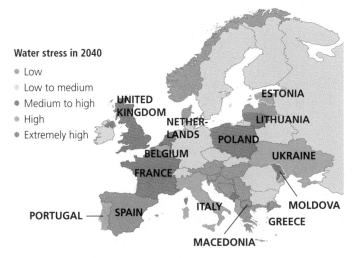

Water stress in 2040

- Low
- Low to medium
- Medium to high
- High
- Extremely high

Figure 2 Water stress levels in Europe in 2040

⊜ This question refers to Figure 2, the map of water stress in Europe by 2040. The risk with this question is that you explain why two or three different places might have extremely high water stress by 2040, e.g. Spain, Greece and Italy. What is actually required is one in-depth explanation using extended points. There are several to choose from including reduced supply because of global warming-induced climate change, or increased demand from rising populations of specific economic activities such as tourism.

Student answer

Mediterranean countries such as Portugal, Spain, Italy and Greece will experience high water stress by 2040 because of climate stress due to global warming. Higher global temperatures will lead to greater evaporation and smaller soil and surface water stores. In addition, shifts in climate belts will mean lower and more unreliable rainfall as climates become more arid, reducing water availability and increasing water stress.

ⓔ 3/3 marks awarded. This is a good answer that takes the idea of global warming as the cause, and expands on it in terms of greater evaporation, changes to rainfall patters and reduced water stores. It is written as a logical sequence of points. Because it uses terminology from the water cycle, it shows understanding of that concept. The key here is to write an extended explanation of a single cause — which this answer does.

(b) Explain how human actions can increase flood risk. (6 marks)

ⓔ This question is focused on human actions, not physical processes. The latter are relevant, but only when linked to a change brought about by human activity — such as decreased infiltration resulting from deforestation. This question is slightly different when compared with part (a) because it would benefit from place-specific detail, i.e. named places where human activity has increased flood risk. Ideally, you should explain two or three human actions in detail rather than try and cover four or five. That approach will tend to produce a descriptive list rather than an explanation (see the mark scheme levels grid for Question 1(b)).

Student answer

Human activity alters the hydrological cycle in a number of ways that can increase flood risk. Widespread urbanisation contributed to flooding in the UK in summer 2007. Summer rainfall totals were the highest for 200 years, but impermeable urban surfaces and urban drainage increased surface runoff in cities such as Sheffield and Hull causing river hydrographs to have reduced lag times and higher peaks. Widespread construction on floodplains decreases their flood storage capacity and places properties at higher risk from even minor flooding. Deforestation reduces interception which slows precipitation's journey to the surface. This in turn reduces infiltration and increases surface runoff. Removal of trees also reduces evapotranspiration, meaning more water enters river systems by surface runoff. Steep slopes in Manila, Philippines, are deforested to create new urban slums. These are prone to flooding and landslides, especially on steep slopes which promote surface runoff. Some estimates suggest that urbanising a previously forested area increases surface runoff from 10% to 55% of precipitation, and reduces evapotranspiration from 40% to 30%.

ⓔ 6/6 marks awarded. This answer focuses in detail on two explanations: urbanisation and deforestation. This is a good approach, especially because some place detail is added for both which shows the student understands flood risk in contrasting locations. The answer recognises that the drainage basin hydrological cycle is the key to understanding increased flood risk. The terminology used focuses on the pathways water takes between reaching the ground and reaching a river channel. There is also a useful link between deforestation and urbanisation in the context of Manila. This answer manages to avoid being a list of problems, and instead is a detailed explanation.

Question 3

Explain why there is uncertainty about future greenhouse gas levels in the atmosphere.   (8 marks)

ⓔ This question needs a detailed understanding of the concept of 'uncertainty' both in terms of human and physical processes. Aim to explain a range of reasons rather than only one or two. This could include uncertainty about future population and affluence levels, as well as uncertainty resulting from mitigation attempts. Physical feedback mechanisms are also relevant. These 8-mark 'explain' questions in both A-level Units 1 and 2 are marked using the following levels mark scheme.

Level 1	1–3 marks	Demonstrates isolated elements of geographical knowledge and understanding, some of which may be inaccurate or irrelevant Understanding addresses a narrow range of geographical ideas, which lack detail
Level 2	4–6 marks	Demonstrates geographical knowledge and understanding, which is mostly relevant and may include some inaccuracies Understanding addresses a range of geographical ideas, which are not fully detailed and/or developed
Level 3	7–8 marks	Demonstrates accurate and relevant geographical knowledge and understanding throughout Understanding addresses a broad range of geographical ideas, which are detailed and fully developed

Student answer

Carbon dioxide levels in 2017 were 400 ppm ⓐ, an increase from 315 ppm in the late 1950s. IPCC projections for 2100 range from 500 ppm to 900 ppm showing there is a large amount of uncertainty ⓑ.

The first reason ⓒ for uncertainty is because greenhouse gas emissions of carbon dioxide, methane and nitrogen oxides are caused by human activities such as farming, industry, electricity generation (fossil fuels) and transport. These emissions result from resource consumption. This is related to both total population and the average level of affluence ⓓ. UN population projections for 2100 range from 8 to 12 billion. Not only is the future number of people not known, but their wealth and ecological footprint can't be known either.

Secondly, efforts to mitigate greenhouse gas emissions could reduce the growth rate of emissions. The 2015 COP21 meeting in Paris ⓔ agreed some emissions targets but these may not be met. On the other hand future agreements could reduce emissions further ⓕ. A business as usual emissions scenario would probably mean carbon dioxide levels of 800–900 ppm by 2100, i.e. people consume resources, especially fossil fuels, in much the same way in the future as they do today.

Thirdly, the response of physical systems such as the carbon cycle to global warming is uncertain. Global warming could increase melting of Arctic permafrost ⓖ which would lead to biological decay of frozen organic material releasing carbon dioxide. In addition, it would release trapped methane — a powerful greenhouse gas. On the other hand warmer temperatures could lead to increased forest growth which would sequester carbon from the atmosphere h. The ocean is the Earth's largest carbon store that has a relatively rapid rate of flux. The oceans could sequester more carbon from the atmosphere in the future but this is uncertain i.

In summary j, the number and wealth of humans, how humans choose to use resources and which resources they use, as well as the response of physical systems to a warmer world are all uncertain.

e **8/8 marks awarded**. These 8-mark questions sit between the 6-mark 'explain' and 12-mark 'assess' questions. They benefit from being organised carefully, and you might want to consider an introductory sentence to focus your answer. In this case there is a starting focus on carbon dioxide levels a with some useful specific data. The answer then clearly states the future uncertainly over carbon dioxide levels b. The structure for the answer comes from three paragraphs, each focused on a different explanation. This gives the answer good range. The first paragraph c focuses on emissions uncertainty, recognising that this is complicated by not knowing either total future population or resources consumption per person d. There is some depth on climate mitigation agreements e as well as recognition that future agreements cannot be known f, therefore creating more uncertainty. The third paragraph broadens the explanation out to include physical systems uncertainty, and recognises physical systems could potentially release or store more greenhouse gas emissions h, i. The summary j is a good way to round the answer off. A judgement is not really needed because the command is 'explain' but the summary completes a well structured answer.

Question 4

Study Table 1. Assess the costs and benefits of Singapore's planned water supply changes by 2060.   (12 marks)

Table 1 Key facts about Singapore's population, water use and water supply in 2016 and planned by 2060

Year	Total population	Water use per person per day (litres)	Four sources of Singapore's fresh water			
			Recycled, treated, grey water ('NEWater')	Desalination	Transboundary water imports from Malaysia	Local rainfall catchments
2016	5.69 million	150	30%	10%	40%	20%
2060 planned	6.56 million	130	55%	30%	–	15%

e This question is a data stimulus question. Your answer must refer in detail to the information in Table 1: quote it in your answer. Table 1 needs some careful analysis first. It shows a major change in how Singapore will get its water by 2060 with some sources increasing, and others even disappearing. Both costs and benefits need to be covered in a balanced way. Often recalling the words 'social, economic, environmental and political' helps to structure an answer to a costs and benefits question (or advantages and disadvantages). As the command is 'assess' your answer needs to weigh up the different costs and benefits and start to consider whether some are more significant than others. This is required for a good level 3 answer. These 12-mark 'assess' questions in both A-level Units 1 and 2 are marked using the following levels mark scheme.

Level 1	1–4 marks	• Demonstrates isolated elements of geographical knowledge and understanding, some of which may be inaccurate or irrelevant • Applies knowledge and understanding of geographical information/ideas, making limited logical connections/relationships • Applies knowledge and understanding of geographical information/ideas to produce an interpretation with limited relevance and/or support • Applies knowledge and understanding of geographical information/ideas to make unsupported or generic judgements about the significance of few factors, leading to an argument that is unbalanced or lacks coherence
Level 2	5–8 marks	• Demonstrates geographical knowledge and understanding, which is mostly relevant and may include some inaccuracies • Applies knowledge and understanding of geographical information/ideas logically, making some relevant connections/relationships • Applies knowledge and understanding of geographical information/ideas to produce a partial but coherent interpretation that is mostly relevant and supported by evidence • Applies knowledge and understanding of geographical information/ideas to make judgements about the significance of some factors, to produce an argument that may be unbalanced or partially coherent
Level 3	9–12 marks	• Demonstrates accurate and relevant geographical knowledge and understanding throughout • Applies knowledge and understanding of geographical information/ideas logically, making relevant connections/relationships • Applies knowledge and understanding of geographical information/ideas to produce a full and coherent interpretation that is relevant and supported by evidence • Applies knowledge and understanding of geographical information/ideas to make supported judgements about the significance of factors throughout the response, leading to a balanced and coherent argument

Student A

Table 1 shows that Singapore plans to dramatically shift its water supply from imports from Malaysia, towards water recycling and desalination by 2060 **a**. At the same time its population will rise by close to 1 million but water use per person falls by 20 litres per day.

There is a potentially a very large benefit of ending use of imported water from Malaysia **b**. In 2016 40% of Singapore's water came from another country that could reduce or stop the supply. There are examples where water sharing agreements lead to tensions such as in the Nile Basin **c**, so relying on another country for water is potentially risky. However, if the relationship is just an economic one, i.e. Singapore pays Malaysia for water, it could be sustainable **d**. It depends on the price Singapore pays per litre, which could be high and is controlled by Malaysia.

Recycled grey water is an example of water conservation. It has the benefits of using the same water multiple times so reducing demand for new supply. Costs might include complex and expensive collection and treatment systems, plus the public in Singapore may not like the idea of 'NEWater' that has been recently used in someone's shower. Water conservation is also evident in the aim to reduce per capita daily consumption. In the UK this is achieved by more efficient washing machines, dishwashers and showers. It may have the benefit of reducing water bills, as well as preventing increases in water demand **e**.

The shift to 30% of water from desalination has the benefit that Singapore will control this water supply, i.e. rather than Malaysia controlling it. However, desalination has costs **f**. It is expensive to build the plants, and these need a large energy source such as oil or natural gas to run. This means desalination is usually not eco-friendly and has high greenhouse gas emissions. It may make water bills higher, because of the added production costs. However, it does ensure water security.

Rainfall catchments are set to decline by 5% **g**. This might actually mean the volume of water they supply is similar to 2016 because despite the 150 to 130 litre reduction in per person water use, total water demand will rise because of the 800,000 increase in population.

Overall, by 2060 Singapore will have the very significant benefit of being water secure and no longer relying on Malaysia. However, this could come at the economic costs of higher water bills and some environmental costs from desalination **h**.

e **12/12 marks awarded**. This is a good answer. It refers to all of the data in Table 1. The first paragraph makes direct reference to the data **a** and this shows good understanding of it. At the start, **b** there is a clear judgement about the significance of the benefit of Singapore reducing its reliance on water from Malaysia. Some brief reference is made to other transboundary water situations **c** which shows breadth of understanding. Assessment is shown by the counter-argument that getting water from Malaysia may not actually be very insecure at all **d**. The paragraph on grey water recycling/NEWater **e** also covers costs and benefits, showing that the issue is being considered from both sides. Environmental and economic costs are considered in relation to desalination **f**, as well as benefits in terms of a secure water supply. The section on rainfall catchments **g** is very analytical, i.e. it unpicks that data to understand the changing picture of Singapore's water demand and shows good understanding. When the command is 'assess' a final conclusion **h** is always useful, in this case stressing the primary benefit of greater water security for Singapore despite some potential costs.

Question 5

Evaluate the extent to which renewable energy sources can meet future global energy demand.

(e) This is an essay question. As such, detailed place knowledge and understanding in the form of examples and case studies is important. A very good answer cannot be written in only general terms. Answers need to show understanding of what future energy demand might be, as well as a range of renewable sources (wind, solar, HEP) rather than only one in detail. The key to a high mark is understanding that 'evaluate' requires supported judgements to be made. For example, could wind power meet a significant chunk of future energy demand or is it too physically constrained, expensive and intermittent to do so reliably in many places? You need to ask yourself these questions, and provide the answers! Good answers will make conclusions based on different energy sources and different locations. These 20-mark 'evaluate' questions in both A-level Units 1 and 2 are marked using the following levels mark scheme.

Level 1	1–5 marks	• Demonstrates isolated elements of geographical knowledge and understanding, some of which may be inaccurate or irrelevant • Applies knowledge and understanding of geographical ideas, making limited and rarely logical connections/relationships • Applies knowledge and understanding of geographical information/ideas to produce an interpretation with limited coherence and support from evidence • Applies knowledge and understanding of geographical information/ideas to produce an unsupported or generic conclusion, drawn from an argument that is unbalanced or lacks coherence
Level 2	6–10 marks	• Demonstrates geographical knowledge and understanding, which is occasionally relevant and may include some inaccuracies • Applies knowledge and understanding of geographical information/ideas with limited but logical connections/relationships • Applies knowledge and understanding of geographical ideas in order to produce a partial interpretation that is supported by some evidence but has limited coherence • Applies knowledge and understanding of geographical information/ideas to come to a conclusion, partially supported by an unbalanced argument with limited coherence
Level 3	11–15 marks	• Demonstrates geographical knowledge and understanding, which is mostly relevant and accurate • Applies knowledge and understanding of geographical information/ideas to find some logical and relevant connections/relationships • Applies knowledge and understanding of geographical ideas in order to produce a partial but coherent interpretation that is supported by some evidence • Applies knowledge and understanding of geographical information/ideas to come to a conclusion, largely supported by an argument that may be unbalanced or partially coherent
Level 4	16–20 marks	• Demonstrates accurate and relevant geographical knowledge and understanding throughout • Applies knowledge and understanding of geographical information/ideas to find fully logical and relevant connections/relationships • Applies knowledge and understanding of geographical information/ideas to produce a full and coherent interpretation that is supported by evidence • Applies knowledge and understanding of geographical information/ideas to come to a rational, substantiated conclusion, fully supported by a balanced argument that is drawn together coherently

Student answer

Global energy demand is expected to increase by 40–50% from today until 2040 [a]. Almost all of this increased demand is driven by emerging and developing countries. Projections from the US Energy Information Administration suggest there will be almost no growth in energy consumption in developed countries. This means there are really two questions: [b] can renewable energy replace fossil fuel used in the developed world, and can renewable energy be the major source of future energy supply in other countries?

Globally, 80% of energy production today is from fossil fuels. In developed countries this is changing in two ways. Firstly, a switch from coal to natural gas, which is cleaner. Secondly, a shift to renewables, especially wind power. Denmark gets 40% of its electricity from wind power and Germany 10%, but globally it only accounts for 4% of electricity [c]. Wind's intermittent and unreliable nature means that stand-by power stations (usually gas-fired) need to be available to boost supply, which adds to costs. Hydroelectric power (HEP) has been widely developed in some countries [d]. However, it requires specific geographical conditions, i.e. a reliable water supply and valleys that can be flooded to create HEP reservoirs. Canada, Brazil and Norway all generate over 50% of their electricity from HEP. Most developed countries have already utilised suitable sites and have limited capacity to expand. This is not the case in some developing and emerging countries such as Ethiopia and China, where it is rapidly expanding.

Developing and emerging country demand is often met by constructing new coal, gas or oil power stations. This is because they are cheap (especially coal), the technology is relatively simple and they can be constructed quickly. Renewable alternatives have disadvantages in comparison [e]. Wind and solar power are more expensive and intermittent. HEP has long construction times and frequently involves the displacement of people to create reservoirs. Nuclear power is technically very difficult, and at up to $10 billion for one power station has very high initial costs. Cost is usually the key variable, and this makes it likely that coal and gas will be the most used fuels to meet demand in the future [f]. BP expects coal demand to increase by about 30% to 2035. China does show what is possible. In 2016 it was the world's largest user of wind power. Capacity increased from 1250 MW in 2005 to 150,000 MW in 2016, but wind still accounted for only 4% of China's total electricity generation [g].

It is very questionable whether renewable energy will replace crude oil used to make transport fuels (petrol, diesel, bunker oil) that accounts for 25% of global energy use [h]. Renewable alternatives are not well developed. Biofuels can replace petrol and diesel, but they require large areas of land to grow crops, which are increasingly needed to feed a growing world population. Electric vehicles are mostly charged by power stations burning fossil fuels. They could be powered by renewably generated electricity but that is along way off in most countries.

In conclusion [i], in developed countries renewable energy will increase its share of energy use, but total demand is static because of improving efficiency. In the developing and emerging world renewables will not meet future demand as long as fossil fuels are a cheaper option. There will be exceptions, in some countries with the right physical conditions for wind, solar or HEP. Transport fuel demand is likely to be met by crude oil supply for the foreseeable future because no viable alternative currently exists that is widespread.

ⓔ 20/20 marks awarded. This is a strong, well supported answer. From the start **a**, it shows understanding of 'future global energy demand', recognising that future demand will not be the same everywhere. This is turned into a structure **b** for the answer by posing two sub-questions about the developed versus the developing/emerging world. This shows that the student recognises that future demand is complex. There is a detailed discussion of wind power **c**, its pros and cons, and the extent to which it has grown in some countries. This section is evaluative because it considers the limitations of wind power and other renewables, especially in terms of their geographic limitations **d** and economic cost **e**. Cost is identified as the most significant variable in the choice of which energy sources to use **f**, which involves making a judgement, i.e. evaluating. The detail on China is a useful example that adds depth to the answer **g**. The section on transport fuels **h** makes a strong argument against a renewable future. This type of clear argument is much better than sitting on the fence, and shows the student is prepared to 'take the question on'. There is a clear conclusion **i**, which returns to the theme from the introduction that future demand in the developed and developed world need to be considered differently. The answer is evaluative throughout, makes supported judgements and has a clear conclusion.

Question 6

Evaluate the extent to which transboundary water sources always lead to conflict between different players.

(20 marks)

ⓔ This essay question is phrased in a very common way, but within it there is a 'trap'. This is that it is very easy to argue 'yes, they always lead to conflict'. After all, there are many case studies (River Nile, Aral Sea, River Ganges, Colorado River) where water is not easily shared and conflict has resulted. On the other hand there are numerous examples of water sharing agreements. These are equally relevant to the question and should be used to present the other side of the argument before coming to an overall conclusion. Remember that 'conflict' means disagreement as well as 'war'. Most of the conflicts over water supply are wars of words, not actual war. Again, detailed place information is important to write a supported argument and conclusion (see the mark scheme levels grid for Question 5).

Student answer

Transboundary water sources are those that are shared across a political boundary **a**. This includes river drainage basins, underground aquifers and lakes. Many transboundary sources straddle an international boundary such as the River Nile, but they include rivers such as the Colorado in the USA that crosses the political boundaries of US States. The UN has identified 276 transboundary international rivers **b** and over 200 aquifers.

In most cases, transboundary water supplies do not lead to conflict **c**. According to the UN, over 450 water sharing agreements have been signed in the last 200 years. Since 1966 **d** the 'Helsinki Rules on the uses of the waters of International Rivers' have provided a legal framework to help countries resolve disputes and share water equitably. These rules were updated in 2004 to the 'Berlin Rules'.

Where conflict does exist, it ranges on a spectrum from mild, diplomatic disagreement to the very rare situation when water becomes a source of open conflict **e**. In most cases, conflicts sour relations between countries. Where conflicts do exist, almost always they occur in places of existing water stress, and where other non-water-related political factors exist.

Long-standing conflict exists between India and Bangladesh over the River Ganges **f**. Low river flows in downstream Bangladesh are blamed on deforestation in the Indian Himalayas. High water pollution levels result from India using the Ganges as a human and industrial sewer. The construction of the Farakka Barrage in 1972 allowed India to divert 10% of the Ganges' flow towards Calcutta, causing reduced water availability in Bangladesh. Broader political relations between Hindu India and Muslim Bangladesh have never been good, so conflict over the Ganges has to be seen in this context **g**. A new 30-year agreement was reached in 1996, showing that some progress on sharing could be made.

In Egypt and Sudan water is a precious resource. Cairo in Egypt receives only 25mm of rainfall per year and the country depends almost entirely on the River Nile for its water supply **h**. Historic agreements from the colonial era gave Egypt and Sudan rights to all of the Nile's waters. Today, these do not reflect the reality of population or development in upstream countries such as Ethiopia and Uganda. Upstream countries signed the Nile Basin Initiative in 1999 but Egypt and Sudan refused to be involved. Increased water usage upstream, and HEP dams in Ethiopia, risk reducing Nile River flows reaching Egypt and Sudan. This is increasingly a source of tensions and, long-term, could lead to open conflict, especially if Egypt feels its only water supply is threatened. A similar situation exists on the Mekong River in Asia **i**. Upstream dam construction by China risks the water supply to downstream Vietnam, Laos and Cambodia. The latter countries are part of a water-sharing treaty called the Mekong River Commission, but China is not. In both the Mekong and Nile cases the long-term solution is for all transboundary basin countries to enter into an agreement based on the existing Berlin Rules.

Transboundary water supplies have contributed to armed conflict only once **j**. Between 1964 and 1967 there were a series of military clashes between Israel and its Arab neighbours (Syria, Palestine) over control of the River Jordan. Even this conflict has had some resolution and Israel and Jordan signed a water sharing agreement in 1994.

In conclusion **k**, it is not the case that transboundary water supplies always lead to conflict. There are more examples of water sharing agreements than conflicts, and recognised international frameworks for resolving disputes. Where conflict does exist it exists as part of wider political disputes, and almost always in places with limited water supplies and no alternative supply.

e **20/20 marks awarded**. This is a well-supported answer that applies examples and case studies effectively to answer the question. Beginning with an extended definition **a** of 'transboundary' is a good way to start, as it focuses the answer on the key topic of the question. Factual detail from the UN **b** adds weight to this. The answer begins by setting out its argument **c**, that transboundary water situations are more often managed than lead to conflict. This helps avoid the answer becoming a list of 'my next example of conflict is'. The section on international rules **d** helps justify the stated argument. Defining conflict **e** is also sensible, as it shows understanding of the concept, i.e. it is much more than simply 'war'. The case study on the River Ganges **f** has the right level of detail so it avoids being descriptive. Towards the end of this section there is an evaluation **g** that recognises the existence of an agreement — which supports the idea that conflicts can be resolved. The level of detail provided on the River Nile **h** is about right, and the use of the Mekong example **i** is good as it supports the argument being made about the Nile, i.e. that conflict exists when all parties are not part of an agreement. The River Jordan example **j** makes the useful point that physical conflict is very much the exception not the norm. The final judgement **k**, that transboundary water conflicts exist when there are water shortages and/or pre-existing unrelated political issues, recognises the complexity of the situation.

Superpowers

Question 7

(a) **Explain why TNCs are an important source of global influence for superpowers.** (4 marks)

e This is a short, point-marked question. It is very important not to turn it into a mini-essay about TNCs. The focus is on the role of TNCs in terms of superpower influence, a much narrower topic than the role of TNCs in globalisation, for instance. The focus of an answer should be on the way TNCs project the culture and values of some countries, and how they generate economic wealth which can in turn be used to fund other sources of power via taxation. Think of these questions in terms of writing two extended explanations to gain 4 marks.

Student answer

Most well-known, global TNCs and their brands are from the USA: Nike, Apple, McDonalds and Disney. TNCs are an important source of the USA's wealth. Apple's US$215 billion sales in 2016 means it pays taxes to the US government that are then used to fund the USA's military power. TNC brands help spread American values and ideology, i.e. consumerism, personal freedom, and this is a major source of cultural influence and soft power. An example is the ubiquity of Disney films worldwide.

e **4/4 marks awarded**. This answer has two extended points. The first focused on the economic role of TNCs, and the second on their cultural role. In both cases the points are extended by the use of examples to reinforce the explanations being given. The answer avoids drifting into defining TNCs or their wider role in globalisation, and focuses on their role in power.

(b) Assess the extent to which China is a threat to the status of the USA as the dominant superpower. (12 marks)

ⓔ This is an essay question, which requires an answer that weighs up both sides of the argument. China does possess some characteristics that challenge the USA such as its total GDP, increasingly its military power and its geopolitical influence. On the other hand, per capita wealth, global TNCs and cultural influence are areas of weakness for China. A strong answer will provide evidence of the strengths and weaknesses of China in the context of those of the USA, then come to a view as to how far China is a threat. There is some room in this question to mention other emerging powers such as India, but only briefly. These 12-mark 'assess' questions in both A-level Units 1 and 2 are marked using the following levels mark scheme.

Level 1	1–4 marks	• Demonstrates isolated elements of geographical knowledge and understanding, some of which may be inaccurate or irrelevant • Applies knowledge and understanding of geographical information/ideas, making limited logical connections/relationships • Applies knowledge and understanding of geographical information/ideas to produce an interpretation with limited relevance and/or support • Applies knowledge and understanding of geographical information/ideas to make unsupported or generic judgements about the significance of few factors, leading to an argument that is unbalanced or lacks coherence
Level 2	5–8 marks	• Demonstrates geographical knowledge and understanding, which is mostly relevant and may include some inaccuracies • Applies knowledge and understanding of geographical information/ideas logically, making some relevant connections/relationships • Applies knowledge and understanding of geographical information/ideas to produce a partial but coherent interpretation that is mostly relevant and supported by evidence • Applies knowledge and understanding of geographical information/ideas to make judgements about the significance of some factors, to produce an argument that may be unbalanced or partially coherent
Level 3	9–12 marks	• Demonstrates accurate and relevant geographical knowledge and understanding throughout • Applies knowledge and understanding of geographical information/ideas logically, making relevant connections/relationships • Applies knowledge and understanding of geographical information/ideas to produce a full and coherent interpretation that is relevant and supported by evidence • Applies knowledge and understanding of geographical information/ideas to make supported judgements about the significance of factors throughout the response, leading to a balanced and coherent argument

Student answer

The world currently has a uni-polar structure ⓐ, with the USA as the dominant hyperpower. This situation has existed since the end of the Cold War in 1990 when the USSR collapsed along with the bi-polar world that had existed since 1945. China is the emerging power closest to the status of the USA in terms of economic, military, cultural and political power ⓑ. Over the next 20 years China is likely to increasingly challenge the USA's hegemony, however, like the USA, some of its pillars of power are stronger than others.

Economically China has experienced annual GDP growth rates of 6–10% since the early 1990s and its total GDP of US$12 trillion is the second largest in the world after the USA's US$18 trillion. However, Chinese income per person is much lower at around US$8,000 compared with the USA's US$55,000 c. In addition, the USA has a larger number of global TNCs, especially ones that operate globally-known brands such as Apple, Nike and CNN. Not only do these TNCs generate wealth but they are culturally influential d, spreading USA values and ideology worldwide. China's TNCs are state-owned enterprises such as banks, oil and mining companies that lack a global profile and therefore have little cultural influence. That said, China is a key location in the global production chain for most global manufacturing TNCs and so is a crucial part of the globalised economy e.

The strength of the USA economy allows it to invest heavily in military technology f. The USA spends US$580 billion each year on its military and defence, compared with US$130 billion in China. USA military assets are deployed worldwide. It has naval bases in Japan and Italy, a fleet of aircraft carriers and nuclear armed missiles. The USA has genuinely global military reach which China does not posses and is unlikely to in the near future. A combination of military power and the cultural influence of the USA through brands and global media mean its ideology is the hegemonic one g.

There are reasons to believe that China is a threat h. Its highly educated workforce is increasingly urban and shifting towards high value service industries. China has invested heavily in modern infrastructure such as a network of 20,000 km of high speed rail. By 2030 its economy could be larger than that of the USA, providing China with the economic power to create a global military system. On the other hand China relies on natural resource imports such as iron ore and oil, which weaken its ability to operate independently.

China's key weakness is its limited geopolitical role i. Whereas the USA tends to operate as the 'global policeman', intervening in conflicts and crisis response worldwide, China tends not to get involved in geopolitics in places that are beyond its immediate borders. The USA is seen as a global leader by other countries. Conversely, China might be viewed as avoiding getting dragged into costly, dangerous situations such as the Afghanistan conflict 2001–2014 and Syrian conflict 2011–ongoing.

Overall, China is not today a threat to the USA's status as a global hegemon, but it is likely to achieve the economic power to be a threat within the next few decades j. It will then need to decide whether to act as a global player in geopolitical and military terms and impose its ideology worldwide as the USA does today.

e **12/12 marks awarded**. This answer shows good conceptual understanding by using terminology such as uni-polar and hyperpower a. The introductory paragraph also uses the idea of 'pillars' of power b, which provides a structure to consider the strengths and weakness of China in comparison with the USA. The section comparing the two country's economies has a lot of factual detail c, which is significantly better than just using words such as 'bigger' and 'smaller'. Hard evidence helps build your argument. There is a good link made between the economic power of TNCs and their cultural influence Ⓓ, which shows an understanding of complexity. Although the answer argues that China is weaker economically, it also recognises China's economic strengths ⒠, which shows the answer is weighing up (assessing) China versus the USA. An outline of the USA's military power ⒡ is then linked to its economic/cultural influence ⒢ to strengthen the point that the USA's status is not really challenged by China currently. China's strengths are also considered ⒣ as well as some of its weaknesses ⒤. These paragraphs show that the answer is a genuine assessment attempting to come to a view on how far China is a threat. This is much more than just a list, because it uses evaluative language and phrases such as 'however' and 'on the other hand'. There is a clear conclusion ⒥. As the command is 'assess', a very detailed conclusion is not needed but a succinct one is useful to make it clear to the examiner what your answer to the question is.

Question 8

Assess the extent to which the rise of emerging powers has led to increased global geopolitical tensions.

(12 marks)

ⓔ This is an extended writing question marked in three levels. This means you need to provide evidence in the form of examples and case studies of emerging powers and how their rise may (or may not) be leading to tensions. Place-based information is important here. The Middle East and South China Sea are both locations of tension that could be mentioned. Three located examples would provide a good range. You need to be careful not to include all possible examples of geopolitical tension. This is because to do so would produce a very long, descriptive answer. The skill is to be selective and choose enough examples to provide sufficient range and depth. To fully answer the question, you also need to consider whether mechanisms (such as the UN) exist to reduce tensions and allow countries to work together (see the mark scheme levels grid for Question 7b).

Student answer

The concept of spheres of influence ⒜ is a useful one when considering tensions between powerful countries. Many countries consider an area beyond their actual border as a region they should have some say over. As emerging powers such as the BRICs become more powerful, and the world becomes more multi-polar, it is likely that these spheres of influence might overlap ⒝, leading to increased tensions.

When the Cold War ended in 1990 the Russian economy collapsed and its economic and political power weakened dramatically. It has taken two decades to recover. Russia considers its western border with Europe its sphere of influence and a more powerful, confident Russia led by Vladimir Putin has come into conflict with the EU and NATO to the west. Russia's invasion of parts of Georgia in 2008 and Ukraine in 2014 ⒞ has created a region of tension from the Baltic to the Black Sea, with Russia determined to prevent Western influence spreading further east.

The quest for natural resources ⒟, especially oil, has created areas of tension and overlapping spheres of influence. This is the case in the Arctic Ocean ⒠

---

where the USA and Russia are both keen to exploit oil and gas, but there is uncertainty over which countries have the right to exploit which areas. China has expanded its operations in the South China Sea by constructing artificial islands to 'stake its claim' over disputed areas — some of which might contain oil and gas. The Middle East contains 60% of the world's known oil reserves and is a constant source of tension. Since 2012 Russia has been involved in the Syrian conflict which has made already complex Middle Eastern politics even more challenging **e**. Tensions can also arise from economic change. China has been accused of widespread patent infringement and producing counterfeit goods. This infringes international Intellectual Property law and is a cost to companies that have designed products, such as Apple, and developed new technologies **f**. It leads to international trade tension between China and the USA/EU.

In theory, global IGOs such as the United Nations exit in order to reduce tensions by bringing countries together to work out their differences diplomatically **g**. In reality the UN is often not very effective. Its key decision-making body, the Security Council, tends to divide along east–west lines, leading to stalemate between the USA, France and the UK on one side and China and Russia on the other.

In conclusion **h**, the rise of emerging powers does seem to lead to increased tensions. As countries gain economic and political power they begin to exercise their perceived 'rights' over a nearby sphere of influence which increases the chances of tensions with other countries. The search for natural resources can also create tensions, as in the Arctic and South China Sea. While there are international organisations that could reduce tensions, such as the UN, they tend to be least effective when the world's most powerful countries are in conflict.

e **12/12 marks awarded** An answer to this question could easily become an extended list of places where superpowers and emerging powers come into conflict with each other. This answer begins with a concept, rather than a case study. The concept of spheres of influence **a** is a useful way of viewing examples of tension and shows the student can do more than just describe case studies. There is good understanding of how changing spheres of influence could increase tension **b**. The case of Russia's western border **c** is useful and there is some place-specific detail on tensions. The section on natural resources **d**, especially oil, has both range and depth. A number of examples are used in this section (**e** South China Sea, Arctic, Middle East) which together show that tension over natural resources is common. Using these three examples produces a much stronger argument than using only one major case study, because it shows that emerging powers quite frequently generate tensions over resources, i.e. an assessment of extent. The section on Intellectual Property **f** shows another source of tension, not based on places, which broadens the assessment out to show range of understanding. There is also the flip-side of the argument that IGOs should be able to reduce tensions but often cannot **g**. Lastly, there is a clear but concise conclusion **h**. Any question worth 8 marks or more will benefit from this, but it is a requirement of the 12-mark 'assess' and 20-mark 'evaluate' questions.

Knowledge check answers

Knowledge check answers

1 It has no external inputs or outputs.
2 Changes in mean annual precipitation or temperature.
3 Rivers and lakes (natural and artificial).
4 It affects temperatures and therefore rates of evaporation and transpiration.
5 Throughflow is through the soil; groundwater flow occurs below the water table.
6 Less runoff; more infiltration, throughflow, evaporation and transpiration.
7 Precipitation likely to exceed potential evapotranspiration throughout the year.
8 The Yenisei has a single, accentuated peak, produced by summer snowmelt and summer rain. The Rhône shows a much less accentuated summer peak produced by snowmelt in summer and winter rainfall.
9 Anything that delays or reduces runoff — vegetation cover, depth of soil, gentle slopes.
10 Local residents, local government officials (planners, engineers, etc.), developers, insurance companies.
11 (a) India and SE Asia; (b) west coast of South America.
12 Population growth, because this increases the other three factors.
13 Intense orographic rainfall; steep slopes and fast runoff.
14 Through tsunamis; vulcanicity beneath glaciers and ice sheets; blocking of rivers by lava flows and landslides induced by earthquakes.
15 Hard engineering works against nature, soft engineering with nature.
16 Important factor in determining vegetation cover and agricultural productivity.
17 Oceans.
18 India, Pakistan, Sudan, Somalia and South Africa.
19 The volume of accessible water resources in a country or region.
20 The competition and potential conflict between those countries with shared rivers.
21 Water needed to sustain higher living standards — more water for washing, cleaning and cooking; more recreational use of water (gardens, swimming pools).
22 Jordan: Syria, Lebanon, Jordan and Israel; Tigris-Euphrates: Turkey, Syria and Iraq; Indus: India and Pakistan; Ganges: Bangladesh and India.
23 High capital costs and technological input; not every country has a coast.
24 Store: atmosphere (sedimentary rocks, soil, etc.); flux: photosynthesis (transpiration, burning, etc.).
25 Biological, physical and carbonate.
26 Climate, vegetation cover, soil type and land use.
27 Carbon dioxide, methane and nitrous oxide.
28 Photosynthesis.
29 Coal, lignite, crude oil and gas.
30 Plants and animals are adapted to survive in particular environments. Climate is a major environmental factor. So when climate changes, so do the related flora and fauna.
31 Energy resources that are capable of being exploited, given the level of demand and available technology.
32 Irrigation, horticulture and intensive livestock rearing.
33 Forms of waste that can be re-used to produce more energy, e.g. nuclear fuel; heat from manufacturing processes, etc.
34 It is clean and easily moved by transmission cables.
35 Much modern technology is energy-consuming. Rising standards of living usually result in more energy-consuming appliances in the home.
36 Because the USA has much larger accessible reserves of fossil fuels than France.
37 More accessible fields becoming exhausted; price of oil does not warrant exploitation of less profitable fields.
38 Usually on the grounds of unsightliness; noise in the case of wind farms.
39 Deindustrialisation.
40 A carbon sink has the ability to absorb carbon dioxide; a carbon store has the ability to retain carbon for varying periods of time.
41 Taiga forest more extensive and only exploited for its timber.
42 A point in time when change becomes irreversible and moves from one stable state to another.
43 The short-wave solar radiation that is reflected from the Earth back into space.
44 Land-use planning examples: soft-engineering – restricting development in vulnerable areas; hard engineering – building structures to make areas less vulnerable.
45 Improving energy efficiency or carbon taxation.
46 Climate change is a global problem; no one country can mitigate it. It needs coordinated international action.
47 28.
48 Russia.
49 The 1991 and 2003 invasions of Iraq, or Russia's actions in Ukraine (2014) or Georgia (2008).
50 1945–1990.
51 Around 15% of global GDP.
52 Russia, China or Japan.
53 The World Trade Organization.
54 The Chinese government.
55 The USA.
56 NATO.
57 China.
58 US$10–100.
59 The USA and Russia.
60 Crimea, part of Ukraine.
61 Democracy in India, communism in China.
62 Iran and Saudi Arabia.
63 Ageing populations.
64 Development assistance/Foreign Aid budget.

Note: **Bold** page numbers indicate definitions of key terms.

Index